Joint WHO/FAO/UNEP/UNCHS Panel of Experts on Environmental Management for Vector Control

Guidelines for
Forecasting the Vector-borne Disease Implications of Water Resources Development

**Prepared by Martin H. Birley, Ph.D.,
Department of Medical Entomology
Liverpool School of Tropical Medicine
Pembroke Place, Liverpool L3 5QA**

The Department of Medical Entomology of the Liverpool School of Tropical Medicine is a
WHO/FAO/UNEP/UNCHS Collaborating Centre for Environmental Management for Vector Control

**Second edition, 1991
PEEM secretariat, WHO, Geneva**

WHO   FAO   UNEP   UNCHS (Habitat)

Acknowledgements

The author would like to acknowledge the detailed suggestions and criticisms provided by Mr E. Potts and the contributions made by Drs M.W. Service, R.W. Ashford. H. Townson, J.D. Davies, D. Bell, J. Jewsbury, D. Smith and J. Nguma. Drs R.J. Tonn and R. Bos of the PEEM secretariat and Dr R. Slooff, Director of VBC, remained encouraging throughout. Many anonymous referees made invaluable comments and suggestions about successive drafts of the manuscript. Errors and omissions remain the responsibility of the author.

About PEEM

The Panel of Experts on Environmental Management for Vector Control (PEEM) was established in 1981 according to the Arrangements agreed upon by its three participating organizations, WHO, FAO and UNEP. In 1991 these Arrangements were revised and the three organizations were joined by UNCHS.

The objective of PEEM is to create an institutional framework for effective inter-agency and intersectoral collaboration by bringing together various organizations and institutions involved in health, water and land development, human settlements and the protection of the environment, with a view to promoting the extended use of environmental management measures for vector control within health programmes, and in development projects as health and environmental safeguards.

The PEEM guidelines series incorporates technical documents, prepared on the recommendation of the Panel, providing information on vector-borne disease problems, prevention and control associated with water resources development. Members of its target audience are not normally reached by more conventional, sectoral outlets. The guidelines are intended as tools to assist non-health professionals in a more health conscious approach to the planning, design and execution of water resources development. Other publications in the series (at the time of printing) are:

- Guidelines for the incorporation of health safeguards into irrigation projects through intersectoral cooperation (M. Tiffen, 1989; second edition 1991, under number WHO/CWS/91.2).
- Guidelines for carrying out cost-effectiveness studies of vector control operations (A. Mills, M. Phillips and C. Dye, in prep.).

About the author

Dr M.H. Birley has a B.Sc. (Warwick) and M.S. (Illinois) in engineering science and a Ph.D. and D.I.C. (Imperial College) in insect ecology. He is a lecturer in medical entomology, a Fellow of the Royal Society of Tropical Medicine and member of the British Ecological Society, the Society of Vector Ecologists, the Institute of Biology and PEEM. His research interests include the estimation of vectorial capacity and the application of knowledge-based systems to environmental health impact assessment.

Table of Contents

Preface

1   The Guidelines

2   What You Need To Know About Vector-borne Diseases

3   A Summary Of Experience

4   References, Glossary and Index

Appendix A: Worksheet 2

Appendix B: Questions Grouped By Specialist

Appendix C: Fact Sheets

Fold Outs

Community vulnerability
Environmental receptivity
Vigilance of health services

Preface

" *I fully realise that health is not the only thing, but that everything else, without health, is nothing, and I think that it is very important to realize this when we look at development at large. Whenever the health component is forgotten, you forget at the same time the vital factor in development, namely the human being, his creative energy, his physical energy.* "

Dr H. Mahler, former Director-General WHO (1982)

" *In the past ten years profound changes have been wrought in our environment. Worldwide deforestation has occurred on a scale never imagined at the time of Alma-Ata, bringing recrudescence of diseases, such as malaria, and destruction of the natural habitat. The excuse for this devastation is development, and the need for food and energy. When the motivation is export-driven, the cost burden in terms of human health and services is never included in the price of the exported commodity, such as rice, lumber and other natural products. Natural resources are irretrievably lost, the health of populations is damaged, and the under-budgeted health services are left to bear the burden. These actions compound the effects of natural disasters, such as flood, storm, earthquake and drought.* "

Dr H. Nakajima, Director-General WHO (1989)

Development of water resources in the tropics and sub-tropics often has a major impact on the environment. One component of that impact is the effect on human health. Several of the most important communicable diseases, such as malaria and schistoso-miasis (bilharzia), are transmitted by organisms (vectors) which depend on water. Water resource development projects lead to either an increase in the number of vectors or the amount of contact between human communities and vectors. The consequence is an increased number of disease cases. Well known examples include the Aswan, Kariba and Volta Lake dams which were constructed to provide economic benefits such as irrigation or hydroelectric power, but which also bestowed additional disease burdens on the local community. During a malaria epidemic in the Gezira scheme (Sudan) 33 working days were lost per tenant, reducing cotton production by an estimated 20%. On the same scheme the prevalence of schistosomiasis has now reached 70%. The development of water resources seems bound to continue, for how else can the quality of life of the majority of the world population be improved? However, a concomitant rise in disease prevalence could significantly reduce the expected benefits.

Two requirements must be fulfilled if such an increase is to be prevented:

- A strong and binding commitment to finance and implement projects which maintain public health and safety, to care for the environment and to consult with and provide adequate resettlement for displaced communities.

- A rapid, simple and cheap procedure for determining whether, and how, the first requirement can be fulfilled.

These guidelines seek to provide a basis for such rapid assessment and to make it available to those without specialist knowledge of health. Water resource development projects are usually planned by economists, agricultural specialists and engineers, debated by politicians and contended by community groups. All of these may wish to consider the potential health impacts of the project and for this purpose seek the collaboration of a local health specialist. The guidelines can only be used to their full potential if links are established, from the very start, with the various departments and government ministries which are concerned with health. We provide guidelines to assess:

- the commonest vector-borne infections which may be encountered;

- the features of the human community which make people vulnerable to these infections;

- the features of the environment which enhance or reduce the risk of transmission;

- the capacity of local health services to respond to this risk.

The vector-borne disease risk can best be reduced by environmental management. Environmental management is intricately linked to project planning. Whereas most health management is a response to existing health problems, water resource development is a planned activity which can, itself, create health problems. Environmental management, in its broadest sense, is concerned with assuring that project design encompasses the need to safeguard health.

Limitations

After a realistic appraisal of environmental health hazards has been obtained, the planner can consider the cost of mitigation and how it may be financed. Such a consideration falls outside the scope of this document. It requires intersectoral collaboration, procedures for monitoring and surveillance, adequate strengthening of health services and appropriate control technologies.

Such a document can only consider the commonest diseases, environments and problems. There will always be local exceptions requiring local specialist knowledge. Similarly, although human health has to be considered as a whole, this document is limited to vector-borne disease and only those vectors whose breeding sites may be disturbed by water development.

Chapter 1

The Guidelines

Who Should Use These Guidelines

This is a workbook for anyone who wishes to make a rapid assessment of the health risks associated with a water development project in the tropics or sub-tropics at the early planning phase. It poses a minimum number of questions in a format which enables a knowledgeable person to obtain approximate answers based on existing information. It is assumed that the user can establish links with key personnel within the national health ministry, who will have informed answers to some, or most, of the questions which they are asked. It is assumed that the assessment is being made in order to plan safeguards, mitigating measures and timely strengthening of health services.

How To Use These Guidelines

- To make an assessment, read Chapter 1.
  (You will be referred to the other chapters as you need them).

- To learn about vector-borne diseases, read Chapter 2.

- For a summary of experience, browse Chapter 3.

- To check the glossary, see Chapter 4.

Scope

The four categories of diseases which are associated with water are indicated in the accompanying figure. Two of these categories are often adversely affected by water development projects. Careful planning of structures and operating schedules, referred to as environmental health engineering and environmental management, can help to prevent or reduce transmission of some of these diseases. Bloodsucking insects acquire pathogenic[1] organisms by biting infected people or, in some cases, infected animals. Transmission may occur when they subsequently bite people. Water contact diseases

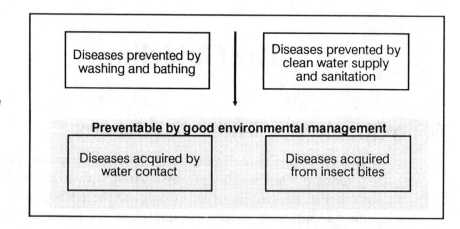

Figure 1-1. The scope of the Guidelines.

depend on intermediate hosts such as water snails. Transmission may occur when people have contact with infected water which contains the intermediate host. The term "vector" will be used in this document in the sense of a biting insect or intermediate[2] host. This definition is sometimes expanded to include animal reservoirs[3]. Eradication of vectors is usually impossible. However, our objective is to reduce or eliminate the clinical disease which is associated with the vector, not the vector itself. In order to achieve our objective the number of vectors or degree of vector or water contact must be reduced. The degree of vector or water contact required to produce clinical disease[4] varies widely. Therefore the degree of vector suppression to be achieved depends on the disease, the locality and the human population.

---

1   disease causing
2   the host occupied by juvenile stages of a pathogenic organism
3   an animal species which carries a pathogen without detriment to itself
4   when a person feels unwell

When To Use The Guidelines

Government-initiated water resource development projects usually start with the identification of potential projects through negotiation between donor, recipient and executing agencies. A series of reports of increasing complexity and detail follow, referred to as feasibility studies. See figure 1-2. During the appraisal phase the donor and recipient complete their negotiations and conclude the financial conditions and proceed to project implementation, construction and operation, which may be accompanied by evaluation and monitoring. After many years of operation a new cycle may

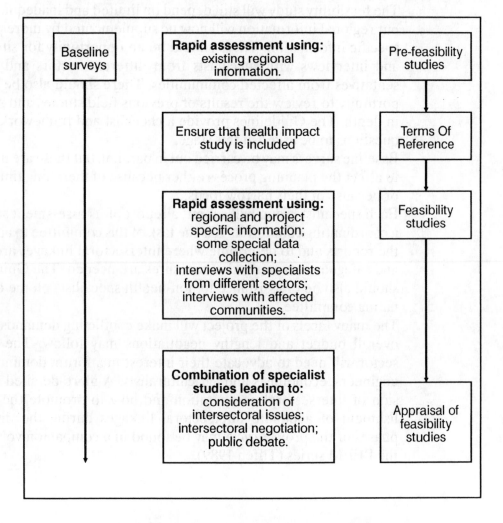

Figure 1-2 Some components of the project cycle.

commence with a proposal for modernization or rehabilitation. All these steps form part of the project cycle.

In the formal terms of the project cycle health impact assessment starts with a rapid survey of existing regional information. Questions to ask during this pre-feasibility study are listed in these Guidelines. They include: which vector-borne diseases occur in the region; what is their relationship to water; what is the capacity of the existing health service? The results of the pre-feasibility study are used to specify Terms of Reference for the more detailed feasibility study. It is vitally important that at least one among the many specialist studies is explicitly concerned with public health.

The feasibility study will still depend on limited and inadequate data but regional information will now be supplemented by more project specific information. There should be an opportunity for site visits and interviews with specialists from different sectors and representatives from affected communities. There should also be an opportunity to review the results of previous field studies and surveys in depth. The Guidelines provide a checklist and framework of the questions to be asked at this stage.

Baseline surveys may be carried out in parallel, but these are unlikely to affect the planning process either because of their long time scale or because of their narrow focus.

Each specialist group will submit a report of its assessment study to a coordinating committee. It is the task of this committee to appraise the reports and to determine where intersectoral linkages are weak and safeguards or mitigation measures are needed. The Guidelines should also be of assistance to non-health specialists on the coordinating committee.

The many facets of the project will make conflicting demands on the overall budget and lengthy negotiations may follow. The health sector will need to advocate their interest in a forum dominated by engineers, economists and agriculturalists. A more detailed discussion of intersectoral co-operation and how to promote the establishment of adequate intersectoral linkages during the different phases of the project cycle may be found in a companion volume in the PEEM series (Tiffen 1989).

Assessment Objective

The objective of the procedure is to complete worksheet 1 (on this page), which indicates whether the hazard associated with each vector-borne disease is likely to be reduced, to remain the same or to be increased at each project phase. Although desirable, a more detailed assessment would require a much larger investment in time and other resources. This worksheet and the reasoning which accompanies it should provide a sufficient basis for comprehending health hazards.

Worksheet 1. The summary assessment.

Project Title	
Project Type	
Location	
Date of Assessment	
Community Group	
Project Phase	

Disease	Vulnerability of community	Receptivity of environment	Vigilance of health services	Health Hazard
Malaria				
Schistosomiasis				
Filariasis				
Dengue Fever				

Assessment Procedure

Figure 1-3 is an overview of the procedure. First, individuals are identified within regional and district departments and research centres who are prepared to answer questions about vector-borne diseases. With the help of these individuals, an inventory is made of the vulnerability of the community to infection, the receptiveness of the environment to disease transmission and the vigilance of the local health services (these terms are explained below). Flowcharts and worksheets provide a focus and structure within which data may be gathered and interpreted. Simple descriptive scores are assigned and much of the procedure is aimed at justifying the assigned scores. A report is prepared which justifies the scores and recommends safeguards and mitigation measures. A collection of such safeguards and measures can be found in the WHO Manual on Environmental Management for Mosquito Control (WHO 1982).

Figure 1-3. An overview of the assessment procedure.

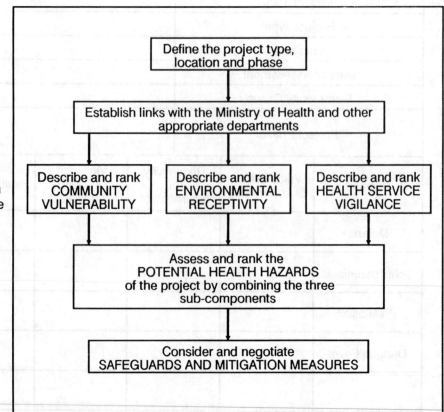

The Ministry Of Health

Before embarking on an assessment of the vector-borne disease implications of a project it is imperative to establish links with the Ministry of Health. Ministries of health are a central government organisation controlling policy, finance and statistics of the health sector. They may stand alone or form part of a larger structure. They contain numerous departments at a national and local level. It will be necessary to identify appropriate individuals and departments with whom to establish contact.

The Ministry of Health usually has a political and an administrative head (Minister and Permanent Secretary) and a technical head, the Director of Medical Services. The technical branches will be headed by Deputy Directors of Medical Services (DDMS). These branches will have responsibility for epidemiology, public health and environmental control. The officer in charge will control one aspect of central government which has regional, district and local medical and health staff. He or she will have information on government-run project centres, relevant research bodies and local government health organisations.

Enquiries should begin at DDMS level to obtain national data and the addresses of relevant project and research centres who should then be approached individually. Local government health departments can normally be approached directly. Further details of the necessary institutional arrangements are discussed by Tiffen (1989).

Three Main Components of the Assessment System

The assessment considers three main components which contribute to the potential health hazard. Because data is sparse and there are great uncertainties, a disease can only be excluded if the vector is absent from the environment, the parasite is absent from the community and neither could be introduced.

Community Vulnerability

The vulnerability of a community to infection depends on the prevalence of that infection in specific sub-groups such as children/adults, males/females or hunters/farmers. It also depends on the proximity to areas where the disease occurs, immune status, previous history of exposure, general health status and the potential effect of an influx of migrants. We seek to score that vulnerability with simple descriptions such as none, low, moderate, increasing or decreasing.

- **Low vulnerability**

This score might be assigned to a community who are unlikely to be exposed to a parasite although it is reported from foci[1] within the region.

- **Moderate vulnerability**

The disease is present in restricted foci at or near the project site. Relatively few people are susceptible or engaged in behaviour which places them at risk of exposure.

- **Increasing vulnerability**

The population is largely susceptible to infection, there is little protective immunity or little experience of the disease and exposure is expected to occur on a large scale. The community may be moving to an area with high prevalence, or changing its major occupation, or infected immigrants may be joining the community.

Environmental receptivity

Environmental receptivity to transmission of the pathogen[2] is determined by abundance of the vector, human contact with vectors or unsafe water and other ecological or climatic factors favouring transmission. Suggested ranks for receptivity include the following:

---

1   Focus/foci: locality where disease is prevalent.
2   an organism or substance which causes disease.

- **Transmission is possible, but is not occurring**

  The vector is present in small foci but there is no human contact or the environment discourages vector breeding at present although this could change.

- **Transmission easily resumed**

  The vector has been eradicated but recolonization is likely if vigilance were reduced, or as a result of the development project.

- **High receptivity**

  There is likely to be an explosive increase in infection. The water development project will create or enhance either vector breeding sites or opportunities for human contact with vectors or unsafe water sources.

Vigilance of the Health Services

Vigilance describes the qualities required of a health service to respond adequately to an increased health hazard. It includes: vaccination campaigns; detection of imported or relapsed cases; drug provision and delivery; hospital beds; sufficient and properly trained personnel; and vector control. Two components of vigilance must be considered separately: prevention and cure. Suggested ranks include:

- **Very good**

  A health service which includes effective preventative measures (such as vector control and chemoprophylaxis[1]) and effective treatment (trained personnel, access, case detection and drug supply).

- **Effective preventative measures only**

  There may be a good residual spraying programme but no supplies of curative medicine or no trained health personnel.

- **Effective treatment only**

  There may be good supplies of medicines and access to trained health personnel, but no vector control measures.

- **None**

  No effective health services of any kind either because there is no infrastructure or because the available health services are over-stretched, under-supplied, unaffordable or inaccessible.

---

[1] medical treatment which prevents illness. An example is the use of chloroquine to prevent infection with malaria.

The Health Hazard

The total health hazard to the community associated with a pathogen completes the disease score. It must be ranked as low, moderate or high or as likely to increase or decrease as a result of the project. There is no simple system to combine the ranks ascribed to vulnerability, receptivity and vigilance. For example, the risk of malaria may increase because there is no effective health service or because there is more vector contact or both. Whatever rank is chosen must be justified by a written explanation as in the example.

For example

The accompanying worksheet (figure 1-4 on page 1- 11) indicates how the assessment might have been completed for the construction phase of an irrigation scheme somewhere in Africa. The summary could be interpreted as follows:

Malaria is expected to represent a health hazard during the construction phase because susceptible people will be exposed to the vector and no preventative measures are planned. A large percentage of the workforce may be incapacitated.

Schistosomiasis does not occur near the project site but a potential vector is present. The health hazard is moderate but will increase unless immigrants or construction workers and their families are screened on arrival for infection, or other preventative measures are instigated.

Onchocerciasis occurs in the region but there is no vector at the project site and none is expected to become established during construction.

Such a summary assessment is insufficient in itself. Each conclusion must be justified by reference to the answers obtained to the questions in the flowchart.

How to Rank Vulnerability, Receptivity and Vigilance

The three components of vulnerability, receptivity and vigilance must, themselves, be ranked by consideration of some subsidiary questions. In the following pages the subsidiary questions are presented in the flowchart format. The flowcharts order the enquiry into a logical structure, indicating why each question is relevant and how the answer could be obtained.

When answering the questions remember that each disease and each project phase will be different.

Figure 1-4. Example of a summary assessment.

Project Title			An example	
Project Type			Commercial irrigation	
Location			Somewhere in Africa	
Date of Assessment			month/year	
Community Group			Construction workers	
Project Phase			Construction phase	
Disease	Vulnerability of community	Receptivity of environment	Vigilance of health services	Health Hazard
Malaria (*falciparum*)	high	moderate	treatment only	high
Schistosomiasis (*mansoni*)	low	moderate	none	low
Filariasis (onchocerciasis)	low	none	none	none

Flowchart Organisation

The flowcharts assume a demand-pull process of interrogation. The user interviews a specialist by asking particular questions rather than the specialist advising the user about what he/she considers important. The questions are directed at different specialists within the Ministry of Health or its equivalent and certain other government departments or institutions. Appendix A contains a checklist of the same questions with a space for answers. Appendix B groups the questions by specialist, enabling the user to plan his interviews. Foldouts at the end of the booklet elaborate the flowcharts and facilitate a step-by-step approach.

The user may have difficulty obtaining reliable answers to some of these questions because of limited time or experience. Guesses may be unavoidable, but this is acceptable providing that they are clearly indicated. Readers of the final report can judge for themselves both the conclusions and the guesses from which they arise.

We would emphasise that even if all the questions are answered the procedure would not approach the norm of a rigorous scientific enquiry.

Each flowchart unit occupies one double page and is accompanied by a short discussion. The questions on the flowcharts must be answered for **each disease** and **each project phase**.

Summary

Worksheet 1 contains a summary of the final assessment. The flowcharts list the questions which have to be answered in order to complete the worksheet. Foldout pages at the end of the booklet provide an outline to follow. The questions may be answered by one of 4 different methods, as appropriate.

- Refer to chapters 2 and 3.
- Ask a specialist.
- Make an informed guess.
- Use previous knowledge and experience.

Community Vulnerability

The vulnerability of a community to infection depends on their proximity to areas where vector-borne diseases occur, their immune status, previous history of exposure, general health status, the potential effect of an influx of infected migrants and the community's main activities. We seek to score that vulnerability with descriptions such as low, moderate, increasing or decreasing.

The acceptable health level of a community depends on political and cultural boundaries and national economic conditions. Advice must be sought from the Ministry of Health.

Prevalence

Prevalence is recorded as the number of positive cases of infection with a pathogen divided by the number of people in the community. Additional terms used include API, ABER and SPR. These are defined in the glossary (chapter 4). Unfortunately, it cannot be assumed that health department records are always reliable.

Well organised health departments will keep maps and graphs indicating the prevalence of various vector-borne diseases.

Drug resistance

Some important diseases, such as malaria, no longer respond to the drugs which used to offer protection or cure. Therefore, it is imperative to determine whether there are foci of drug resistant disease which could undermine the health services associated with the project. Resistance develops rapidly compared to the life of the project.

Parasite or pathogen reservoirs

There may be a human group who maintain close contact with vector populations because of the place in which they live or because of their occupation. They may provide a potential source of infection to members of other communities.

What you need to know about Community Vulnerability

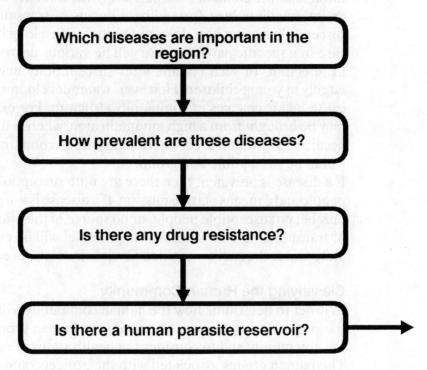

Which diseases are important in the region?

How prevalent are these diseases?

Is there any drug resistance?

Is there a human parasite reservoir?

How you could find out

Annex C contains basic fact sheets about vector-borne diseases. Tables 2-1 and 2-2 list the diseases which you should consider and some notes on their distribution. The accompanying maps indicate distribution within continents. There is always the possibility that an unusual disease is present.

The Health Department and its subsidiaries, such as the Malaria Control Unit, will be able to inform you about relevant diseases, drug resistance and human risk groups.

Susceptibility and Immunity

Transmission of vector-borne diseases depends on the conjunction of three separate elements: the parasite (in an infective host), the vector or intermediate host (providing a means of transmission) and the susceptible human host. In communities with a long history of exposure to a specific parasite there will be various degrees of immunity to infection. In such communities susceptibility may be restricted largely to young children. However, water development projects can cause major changes in community structure. For example, settlers may be brought from a high mountain area, where a disease does not occur, to a lowland area where a disease is common. Such settlers would be susceptible as a group.

If a disease is prevalent then there are both susceptible and infective people and a means of transmission. If a disease is not prevalent there may be: no susceptible people; or no source of infection; or no means of transmission. The transmission potential will be evaluated separately under the section entitled Environmental Receptivity.

Classifying the Human Community

In order to determine how the human community will be affected by the project it is necessary to classify the human groups which form the community and to consider the health status of each group.

The human groups associated with the project could be classified in several ways. It may be appropriate to group together families from the same village or region. Alternatively, it may be appropriate to distinguish the families of construction workers, settlers, spontaneous immigrants and prior occupants of the proposed site and peripheral sites. Table 1-1 suggests a simple classification for resettlement schemes. The age structure of communities associated with development projects is often very different from the national norm because a greater number of children are borne and survive or because settlers are in their prime child bearing years. Immigrants from different regions or different climatic zones may be especially at risk.

The health status of the human groups associated with the project could be affected in many complex ways. For example, settlers may be close to starvation until the first crop is harvested. A number of indicators of well-being are listed in table 1-2. More details may be found in the other documents in this series.

Community Vulnerability continued

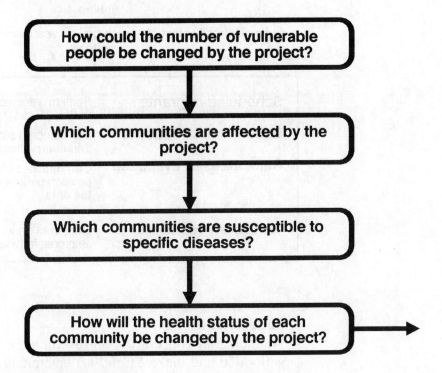

How could the number of vulnerable people be changed by the project?

Which communities are affected by the project?

Which communities are susceptible to specific diseases?

How will the health status of each community be changed by the project?

How you could find out

List the various human communities which are affected by the project. Table 1-1 suggests a simple classification scheme. The project planners will be aware of some, but not all, of the affected groups.

Ask the Health Department about the health status of these communities and how they may be affected by the project. For example, settlers from highland areas may have had no previous exposure to malaria. Find out about the history of any similar projects in the region.

Table 1-1

A simple classification of human groups associated with resettlement projects.

Scheduled migrants	Settlers selected by government
Unscheduled migrants	Self-selected settlers, squatters and encroachers
Relocatees or evacuees	Communities displaced by the project, people already living in the area
Temporary residents	Construction workers and seasonal farm labourers.

For example
Planners may concentrate on resettlement when a valley is flooded and make careful arrangements for the resettlers. However, a fishing community may be attracted by the abundance of fish in the new reservoir. Woodcutters may be attracted by the new communication route allowing access to the hinterland. Such unscheduled migrants may come from distant river basins, bringing new parasites. They will most likely live in unsanitary conditions. The planning document may ignore them completely.

Your most important tool for assessing what could happen is the experience of similar projects in the region.

Table 1-2
Indicators of well-being which may contribute to a communities response to the
challenge of vector-borne disease.

Socio-cultural Indicators

Literacy, educational levels, economic levels, housing standards (construction, piped water), personal and public hygiene, traditional practices considered beneficial/harmful to health, access to and use of clean water (standpipes, protected sources), excreta disposal. Use of bednets, screens and sprays. Purchase of modern medicines and self-medication. Tendency to seek access to modern health care.

Prior Exposure To Each Parasitic Infection

Of primary importance is the presence or absence of the infection among the human groups forming the community. Additional information would include the acquired immunity, tolerance or premunition to the parasite strains encountered; the potential for introducing new species or strains of parasites to the project community; the intensity and prevalence of infection;the rates of morbidity and mortality. Each group may be characterised as non-immune (susceptible), partially immune, totally immune or infectious. Susceptibility may vary seasonally because of sickness and food shortage.

Access To Health Care

Access to physicians, nurses and nurses' aids, hospitals, dispensaries and aid posts within walking distance or otherwise. Distribution of prophylactic medicines (especially for malaria), distribution of curative medicines (malaria, schistosomiasis, filariasis), health education, vaccination rate, functional primary health care.

General Health Indicators

Gastro-intestinal and respiratory infections, nutrition, indices of other parasitic infections, accidents, infant mortality, expectation of life.

Prior Knowledge Of Each Disease

Where there is no significant protective immunity to a parasitic infection a human group may still cope better with exposure to infection because of prior experience, or folk knowledge. The knowledge may reduce distress and fear and may motivate behaviour which limits exposure to infection or may promote indifference.

Human behaviour

Human behaviour has a profound effect on the degree of contact with vectors or unsafe water. Contact can occur near or far from the domestic environment. Contact near the domestic environment often ensures that disease prevalence is more widely distributed between age and sex classes. Contact far from the domestic environment is often associated with economic activities and may restrict disease prevalence to certain age and sex classes.

The economic activites may be associated with the project and could include construction or agricultural work. In these cases, special means of individual protection should be considered. However, villagers usually have a large number of informal occupations in addition to their main occupations.

For example

In South East Asia malaria is now often restricted to the forest and forest fringe. Resettlement projects have sometimes disrupted the rural economy to such an extent that villagers have increased needs for forest produce and increased contact with malarious areas.

Community Vulnerability continued

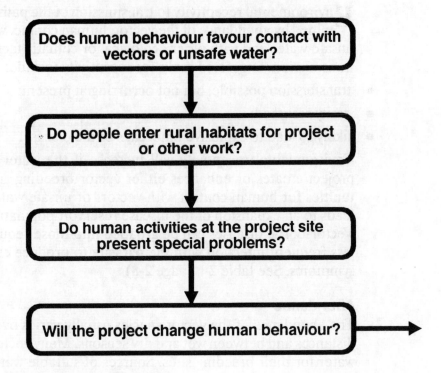

Does human behaviour favour contact with vectors or unsafe water?

Do people enter rural habitats for project or other work?

Do human activities at the project site present special problems?

Will the project change human behaviour?

How you could find out

Consult the human communities associated with the project or their representatives, or specialists such as anthropologists, sociologists and geographers. Determine how the community use natural products obtained by hunting and gathering. Ask whether they keep farms elsewhere.

Do project related activities expose people to special opportunities for vector or water contact either at the project site or elsewhere? Where do people wash? What do they do in the evenings? What are their sleeping customs? Do they use bednets? Could the project change human behaviour by creating new occupations or removing old ones? Will new agricultural techniques be introduced?

Environmental Receptivity

Environmental receptivity to transmission of the pathogen is determined by abundance of the vector, human contact with vectors or unsafe water and with other ecological or climatic factors favouring transmission. Suggested ranks for receptivity include:

- transmission possible, but not occurring at present;
- easily resumed;
- likely to lead to explosive outbreaks of the disease.

Environmental receptivity will increase if the water development project creates or enhances either vector breeding sites or opportunities for human contact with vectors or unsafe water sources, or leads to an expansion of the disease reservoir population.

Vector-borne diseases can be grouped into those requiring more or less frequent infection with the parasite to produce clinical disease symptoms. See table 2-6 (page 2-8).

Abundance

The abundance of the vector species usually varies over quite small distances and between wet and dry seasons. Many vectors depend on water for their breeding sites. Sources of suitable water depend on climate, agricultural patterns and practices and topography.

Abundance may vary with season because breeding sites are reduced or entirely absent during unfavourable climatic periods. Abundance may be restricted to discrete foci where there are patches of favourable breeding sites in a generally inhospitable environment. For example, dry season water holes may harbour and concentrate the abundance of snail hosts of schistosomiasis. There may be seasonal variation in human contact with vectors or water.

Insecticide resistance

Insecticide/pesticide resistance is a severe problem in many areas. Although alternative chemicals are usually available they are often much more expensive than the chemicals to which resistance has developed. Vector control may be diminishing in the project area because of insecticide resistance.

What you need to know about Environmental Receptivity

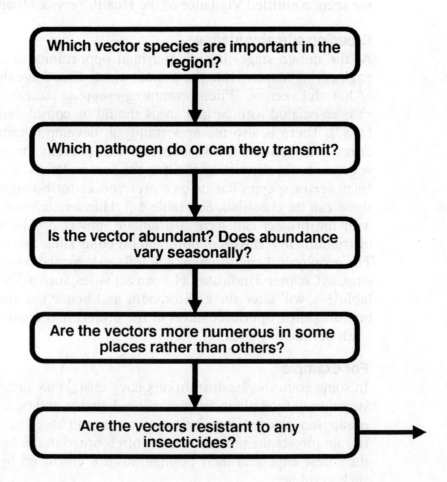

- Which vector species are important in the region?
- Which pathogen do or can they transmit?
- Is the vector abundant? Does abundance vary seasonally?
- Are the vectors more numerous in some places rather than others?
- Are the vectors resistant to any insecticides?

How you could find out

The pathogen responsible for the disease is associated with a specific group of vectors, as listed in table 2-3 (page 2-5). The principal habitat of these vectors is listed in table 2-2 (page 2-3) and the vector's dependence on water is indicated in table 2-4 (page 2-6). The Department of Health or its Division of Vector Control will be able to advise about local vector habitats, their seasonal importance and the status of insecticide resistance.

Changes in vector abundance

Vector abundance is assumed to depend primarily on breeding site availability and chemical control measures, which are discussed in the section entitled Vigilance of the Health Services (page 1-34).

Breeding site abundance

At the design stage there is maximal opportunity to incorporate engineering features into the project which discourage the breeding of harmful vectors. When promoting cropping patterns the health risks associated with certain crops should be considered. See FAO (1987). There is also the opportunity to develop operating procedures and maintenance schedules which prevent the regrowth of vegetation, the deposition of silt or the accumulation of waste water. Each vector species has its own preferences for breeding sites and these can be classified. See table 1-3. Human activities associated with the project can have a dramatic impact on the abundance, distribution and classes of potential breeding sites. See table 1-4.

The geophysical environment will influence availability of breeding sites, as Chapter 3 indicates. Human activities, such as those listed in table 1-4, will alter the environment and hence the abundance of breeding sites. Special features of the project may create additional kinds of breeding sites.

For example

In some countries health workers have mistakenly ordered the destruction of food plants such as maize, bananas and beans under the misapprehension that malaria mosquitoes can breed in them.

In rain forests the malaria vectors often breed in the light shade of the forest edge and their populations are enhanced by tree crops such as rubber.

Pig production in the vicinity of paddy rice cultivation has led to epidemics of Japanese encephalitis.

The abundance of malaria vectors is usually dramatically increased by paddy rice cultivation.

Environmental Receptivity continued

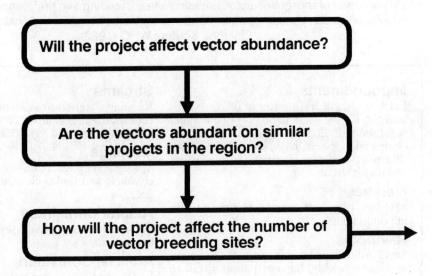

Will the project affect vector abundance?

Are the vectors abundant on similar projects in the region?

How will the project affect the number of vector breeding sites?

How you could find out

Find out what happened on similar projects in the region. Ask the Vector Control Department for detailed information about the breeding requirements of local vectors using table 1-3 as a guide. Inspect the project site, look for potential breeding places and visualise the site in the future. Find out what kind of agriculture is planned and how it will affect degree of shade and changes in stream flow.

Refer to WHO Offset Publication 66 (1982).

Table 1-3

A classification of mosquito vector breeding sites. Breeding site preference may depend on the exact degree of shading, water flow rate, amount of organic material and many other factors. Source: WHO (1982).

Impoundments
Large bodies of fresh water in full or partial sunlight. Larvae occur in floating or emergent vegetation or floatage near the edges. Includes lakes, pools, bays, large borrow pits, slow rivers and pools in drying beds of rivers and major streams.

Marshes
Marshes, bogs and swamps associated with impoundments.

Rainpools
Small collections of seepage water, stagnant and often muddy, but not polluted; full to partial sunlight. vegetation present or absent. Includes roadside ditches, clogged drainage ditches, small borrow pits, wheel ruts, hoofprints, natural depressions and puddles.

Rice fields
Seasonal breeding sites, especially important between transplanting and closure of canopy.

Shaded Water
Partially or heavily shaded water in forests. Includes pools, ponds, swamps and sluggish streams.

Streams
Running water courses, clear fresh water, direct sunlight. Includes lowland grassy or weedy streams and irrigation ditches.

Seepage
Springs, seepage from streams, irrigation channels and tanks; clear water; direct sunlight.

Natural Containers
Plant hollows and cavities; epiphytic arboreal bromeliads.

Artificial Containers
Wells, cisterns, water storage tanks, ornamental basins, tins, plastic packages, abandoned car tyres.

Polluted Water
Heavily contaminated with faeces and other organic waste, foul water; direct sunlight.

Other Breeding sites
Many other categories could be required according to local circumstance.

Table 1-4

A classification of the effect of human activity on the environment in relation to breeding sites of vectors, with emphasis on mosquitoes.

Water Surface
Developments increasing water surface area through the construction of impoundments, water courses and rice fields. Inadequate drainage from settlements and fields and seepage from unlined canals leading to the formation of pools and swamps; variable importance of flow rate and wave action.

Water Table
Developments raising the water table or exposing ground water (e.g. digging shallow wells); developments promoting the formation of permanent pools and contributing to the problem of drainage.

Table 1-4 continued

A classification of the effect of human activity on the environment in relation to breeding sites of vectors, with emphasis on mosquitoes.

Submergence

Development of impoundments and rice fields causing old river banks and vegetation to be submerged and shorelines to be changed.

Water Courses

Construction activity involving stream stoppage and diversion; creation of irrigation and drainage channels. The number, size and length of water courses may be altered and the volume and flow rate of water may change. Water courses may be lined or unlined with steep of shallow sides and open or enclosed in pipes. Seepage water from unlined channels may increase water surface area. The banks of water courses may be affected by trampling and vegetation and this may alter the flow rate and increase seepage and pool formation.

Movement

People, animals and heavy equipment moving into and through the project area. Creation of roads, paths and fords; formation of depressions which collect rain or ground water; deformation of banks of water courses and margins of reservoirs by trampling.

Settlement

Construction and use of temporary housing, with inadequate water supplies, stores and sanitation facilities used by settlers, construction workers and spontaneous immigrants. Provision of permanent housing for settlers which falls into disrepair. Lack of maintenance causing water supplies to be interrupted by pump failure and domestic water obtained from unprotected sources.

Excavation and Cultivation

Construction of roads, canals and ditches, clearance of trees and other vegetation, excavation of borrow pits. Cultivation practises involving ridging, banking or flooding, and causing temporary increases in water surface area.

Aquatic Succession

Developments creating new aquatic habitats which are colonised by a variety of plants and animals. The plants will affect the flow of water and the margins of impoundments. The growth of vegetation may be actively promoted by agriculture (eg seasonal rice transplanting) or passively encouraged by inadequate maintenance such as lack of deweeding activites. The animals may include harmful species such as mosquito larvae and snails and beneficial species, such as larvivorous fish. Both seasonal and longer term successions may occur and reoccur following further disturbances. Temporary inorganic pollution may cause reversion.

Terrestrial Succession

Newly cleared land recolonised by plants and animals including grasses and shrubs and later thickets and trees. The succession may be actively promoted (eg planting of shade trees, annual or perennial crops) or passively encouraged by inadequate deweeding, grazing of domestic animals or needs for fuelwood. The vegetation may provide habitats for wild birds and animals which are potential reservoirs of disease. Seasonal and longer term successions occur and are disrupted by activities such as grass burning.

Organic Pollution

Passive or active contamination of water with domestic and agricultural waste, especially around human settlements. Disrepair of waste disposal systems, overflow of latrines; contamination by urine and faeces of wild or domestic animals contributing to disease transmission.

Inorganic Pollution

Contamination by waste products of construction such as cement, engine oil and silt and agricultural chemicals is detrimental to both vectors and their natural enemies.

Landfill

Raising the level of low lying land for construction may cover surface water and reduce breeding sites. The soil must be excavated elsewhere creating borrow pits.

Colonisation

Most vectors have enormous powers to colonise and recolonise breeding sites. Flying insects can migrate substantial distances, especially when helped by a prevailing wind, see table 1-5. Snails are adapted to seeking passive transport on floating materials in rivers, the legs of animals and on vehicles. If a vector or intermediate host is present in a region it will, sooner or later, colonise or recolonise the breeding sites created by the project.

Table 1-5

The flight range of vectors (kms). Migratory flights are often aided by prevailing winds and occasionally much longer flights have been recorded. Local movement is indicated as a guide to settlement siting. Where a range is indicated, the majority of vectors will only travel the shorter distance.

Vector	Local movement	Migration
Simuliid blackflies	4-10	400
Anopheline mosquitoes	1.5-2.0	50
Culicine mosquitoes	0.1-8.0	50
Tsetse	2.0-4.0	10
Phlebotomine sandflies	.05-0.5	1

Environmental Receptivity continued

> **Could new species of vectors colonise the site from elsewhere?** →

How you could find out

Determine whether any vectors are found upstream or upwind. Do climatic conditions favour long distance vector migration? Is passive migration on vehicles, livestock or boats likely to occur? Where are the communication routes? Have any new bridges or roads created a corridor for additional movement of people, livestock or goods?

For example

There is no schistosomiasis transmission in Sarawak, at present, because there are no snail vectors and no indigenous cases. However, schistosomiasis is prevalent in some localities on the nearby islands of the Philippines and Sulawesi. The vector could be imported on heavy earth-moving equipment used for dam construction.

In South America the construction of roads through rain forests and bridges across rivers is believed to have contributed to the spread of vectors by removing natural barriers to migration.

In West Africa the vector of river blindness regularly recolonises temporary streams during the wet season by flying up to 400 kms aided by the prevailing wind.

Contact Associated with Vector Behaviour

Each species of vector has different habits which determine when, where and under what conditions it bites or associates with people. Important differences include preferred breeding sites and, in the case of vectors, preferred time of feeding (day or night), location (indoors or outdoors) and blood preference (animal or human). See table 1-6. There will often be other vector species which are far less important, because they are not abundant or have less contact with people, but whose importance may increase as a result of the project. For example, tsetse and phlebotomine sandflies often inhabit undisturbed rural environments far from human habitation. They feed on wild animals which may be parasite reservoirs.

Contact can be reduced by reducing the abundance of vectors (by reducing breeding sites) and by changing human behaviour.

Human settlement design

Contact with vectors or unsafe water can occur near or far from the domestic environment. Contact near the domestic environment may be prevented by ensuring that there are no breeding sites in the vicinity. The flight range of vectors was listed in table 1-5.

- Settlements which are 2km or more from rice fields will be largely protected from rice field breeding mosquitoes.

- Settlements with adequate sanitation will be largely protected from mosquitoes which favour foul water.

- Contact with unsafe water is prevented by ensuring that safe water points are more convenient to use.

- Development projects often encourage unplanned urbanization which create many potential breeding sites.

- Domestic water storage often provides breeding sites for vectors of dengue fever.

Environmental Receptivity continued

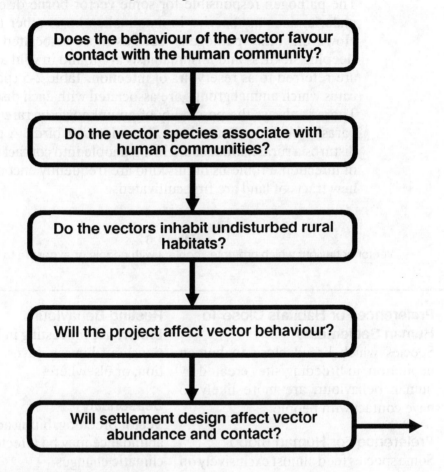

Does the behaviour of the vector favour contact with the human community?

Do the vector species associate with human communities?

Do the vectors inhabit undisturbed rural habitats?

Will the project affect vector behaviour?

Will settlement design affect vector abundance and contact?

How you could find out

Find out from the Vector Control Department whether the vectors live in or near human habitations, in agricultural zones or in undisturbed natural environments. In agricultural zones they may depend on the presence of domestic animals. Will new agricultural techniques be introduced? In natural environments they may depend on the presence of wild animals as in the case of tsetse flies in East Africa. There may be a Game or Wildlife Department which can advise on the abundance and distribution of wild animals.

The project may affect vector behaviour by changing the relative abundance of humans and animals.

Consider settlement design, water supply, sanitation and waste disposal.

Animal Reservoir

The pathogen responsible for some vector-borne diseases, such as malaria, does not survive in mammalian hosts other than humans. However, other pathogens such as those associated with African sleeping sickness and leishmaniasis are found in wild animals which are referred to as reservoirs of infection. Table 2-5 (page 2-7) indicates which animal groups are associated with each disease.

There is always the possibility of an unknown or rare arbovirus[1] or parasite being harboured by wild rodents or birds. A project which disturbs a rural habitat could bring people into contact with a source of infection. Problems of this kind are frequently encountered when new tracts of land are first cultivated.

Table 1-6
Vector behaviour which promotes contact with people or exposure to infection.

Preference For Habitats Close To Human Settlements

Species which breed close to human habitation, in breeding sites created by human behaviour, are more likely to have contact with people.

Preference For Human Blood

Some species feed almost exclusively on human blood while others will only bite people because their usual host animal is scarce.

Contact Sites And Times

Preference for feeding indoors or outdoors; host seeking during daylight, twilight or night.The village, farm and forest may all be different contact sites and the people affected may be related by their occupation.

Resting Behaviour

Preference for resting in human habitations, out-houses, caves, under vegetation, or elsewhere.

Seasonality

Vector breeding, biting activity and host abundance may be affected by seasonal climatic changes.

Survival Of Infective Stage

A vector may not survive the extrinsic incubation period and thus may not contribute to disease transmission.

Association With Domestic Animals

Species with a preference for the blood or habitations of domestic animals may be brought into contact with people who, themselves, live close to domestic animals.

---

1   virus transmitted by insects, ticks or mites.

Environmental Receptivity continued

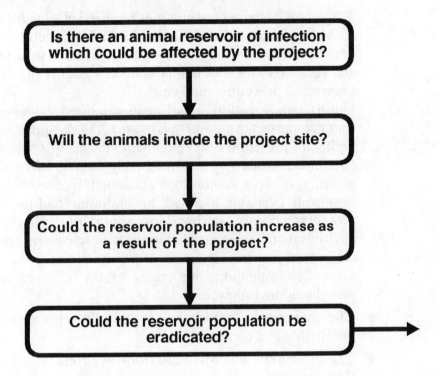

Is there an animal reservoir of infection which could be affected by the project?

↓

Will the animals invade the project site?

↓

Could the reservoir population increase as a result of the project?

↓

Could the reservoir population be eradicated? →

How you could find out

Table 2-5 indicates which diseases are associated with animals. Further information could be obtained from Departments of Health, Environment or Veterinary Science. Determine whether increases in rodent populations have posed a problem in similar projects.

For example

When large areas of the southern steppes of the Soviet Union were developed for agriculture a reservoir of leishmaniasis was discovered in the rodent population. The natural habitat of these burrowing rodents was destroyed by a carefully planned programme of bulldozing and ploughing. Rodents were subsequently excluded by integrated control measures including poisoning and the construction of physical barriers.

Vigilance of the Health Services

Vigilance describes the qualities required of a health service to deal with an increased health hazard. It includes: detection of imported or relapsed cases; drug provision; hospital beds; sufficient personnel; and vector control. Two components of vigilance must be considered separately: prevention and cure.

Unfortunately, health departments are often the last to hear that a water resource development is planned. Consequently, there may be no health provision in resettlement villages or construction camps. Existing facilities may be stretched by immigrants without advance planning of drug supplies or personnel. There may be no health inspectors available to advise on sanitation and no spray teams to protect temporary housing. Most important of all, there may be no environmental safeguards or mitigation measures incorporated in the project plans.

When designing mitigation measures, the following general principles should be followed:-

- The measures should be technically appropriate, culturally acceptable and community-based.

- The community which benefits from the project should play an active decision making role in controlling the adverse effects of the project.

- The burden of adverse effects should not be borne by communities which do not benefit from the project.

- The available health infrastructure and personnel should not be overburdened. The project may have to provide hard currency resources to purchase drugs, equipment, transportation and buildings. Additional training may be required.

Effective medical care

There may be a policy of distributing prophylactic drugs to children, pregnant women and other high risk groups. There may be a system of case detection and treatment but this requires efficient disease surveillance and adequate access to health care facilities. An appropriate system of disease surveillance and control may include the selection and training of village health care volunteers. Training would include blood film preparation and distribution of drugs. Table 1-7 indicates some of the factors associated with medical care.

Vigilance continued

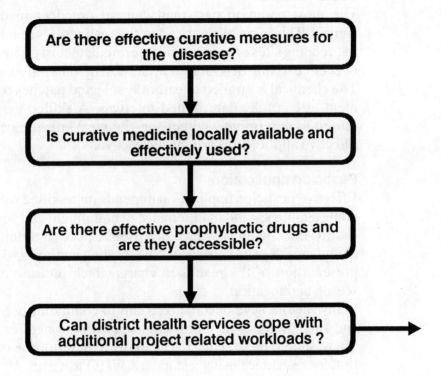

How you could find out

Consult the Health Department. Consider the frequency of spraying, availability of transport, supplies and spare parts.

Vector Control

The most common pest management practices involve chemical control. This is usually applied to the resting sites of adult vectors or to breeding sites of vectors and intermediate hosts. The effectiveness of chemical control is limited by the cost of materials and application. The chemical is applied to carefully selected patches of the environment at carefully determined intervals. A skilled workforce is required to determine whether the chemical kills the pest and where selective applications are most effective.

Pesticide application

Effective pesticide application depends on a skilled workforce, adequate supplies, good maintenance of equipment and susceptibility of pest to the chemicals which are used. Effective monitoring of pest abundance depends on a suitable sampling method and schedule and presentation of the results in charts which indicate abundance by season and location.

Many vectors have become resistant to commonly used insecticides and such methods of vector control may no longer be appropriate. There should be a technical capability to monitor the vector population for resistance using a standard WHO test kit.

Research institutions may be able to provide an independent assessment of the claims made by vector control departments.

For example

Adult female mosquitoes may rest indoors on walls and ceilings so that spraying with a residual insecticide seems to be a cost-effective method of control. However, after spraying for a few years the mosquito may only rest outdoors and is no longer controlled by this method.

What you need to know about Vigilance

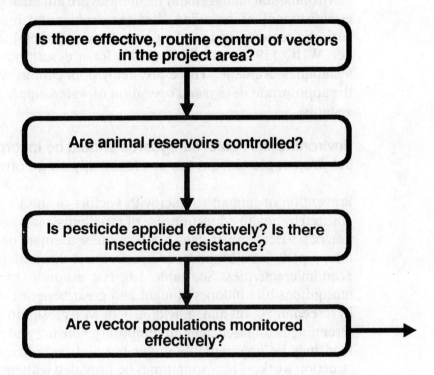

Is there effective, routine control of vectors in the project area?

Are animal reservoirs controlled?

Is pesticide applied effectively? Is there insecticide resistance?

Are vector populations monitored effectively?

How you could find out

Table 1-7 lists some of the factors affecting medical treatment of vector-borne diseases. The Ministry of Health and qualified medical practitioners should be able to provide additional information. Check the supply of drugs in local health centres: are they replenished on time? Are local health workers aware of the project? Is there a health centre near the project site?

Experience has shown that an effective way of ensuring that the health component of a project has adequate budget, continuity and independence is by incorporating it in the overall project budget.

Planning for vector control by environmental management
Environmental management techniques are aimed at preventing the
establishment of breeding sites (environmental modification) or
periodic removal of breeding sites (environmental manipulation).
See WHO (1982) and FAO (1984) for a description of the many
techniques available. There are many publications which consider
the appropriate design and operation of water supply and sanitation
systems.

**Environmental health safeguards should be incorporated in
the project plans from the pre-feasibility stage onwards.**

Prevention of human contact with vectors or unsafe water may be
ensured by health education, use of repellents and screens, construction of barriers and bridges, appropriate settlement design and location, piped water supplies, adequate waste disposal and changes in
economic activities. See table 1-6. For example, many species of
mosquitoes bite indoors at night and great benefit can be obtained
by screening rooms and individual beds with mosquito netting. Room
screening is impracticable in temporary housing and screens of any
kind may be unacceptable under hot and humid conditions. Construction workers may sometimes be provided with protective clothing to prevent contact during their working day.

- New settlements should be constructed to a high standard using
  designs which are appropriate and acceptable to the settlers.
- Homesteads should be grouped to reinforce cultural identity rather
  than alienation.
- There should be adequate supply of safe water and provision of good
  sanitation facilities.
- Settlements should be distant from irrigation ditches and provided
  with safe bathing facilities so as to prevent children from being
  infected with schistosomiasis.
- There should be provision for vegetable gardens and animal pens.
- Access to unsafe water should be limited by the provision of bridges,
  by fencing and by zoning.

Vigilance continued

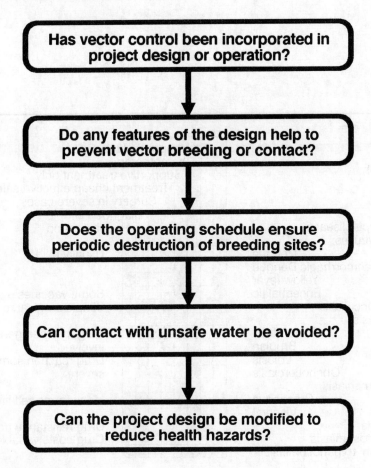

How you could find out

Examine the project plans and operating schedule. Discuss them with the Vector Control Department and project planners. See table 1-6.

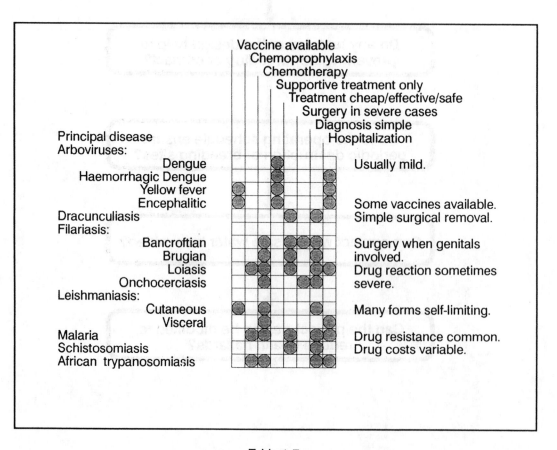

Table 1-7

A broad indication of the factors affecting medical treatment of vector-borne diseases.
There are many additional complications. See references for additional texts.

Chapter 2

What you need to know about Vector-borne Diseases

The Diseases

Appendix C to this document contains a set of basic fact sheets about the main vector-borne diseases which should be considered. A series of tables and maps in this and the previous chapter contrast and compare problems of treatment, distribution, habitat and vector association. The major part of this chapter is concerned with the ecology of the vector in relation to disease transmission. Specialist language has been avoided as much as possible and, where its use was inevitable, the terminology is explained in footnotes. A glossary is provided in chapter 4.

Regional Distribution

The transmission of vector-borne diseases depends on many factors, some of which are not geographically limited. However, the distribution of vectors and reservoir hosts is strictly limited, usually according to zoogeographical[1] boundaries. The main zoogeographical regions are indicated in table 2-1 together with the infections which are naturally transmitted in the region. Generally speaking, the establishment of transmission outside the normal range is very un-

---

1   Global animal distributions.

Table 2-1
A broad indication of the vector-borne diseases naturally transmitted in
each zoogeographical region.

Mexico, Central and South America
Widespread dengue and yellow fever, some bancroftian filariasis, some onchocerciasis, widespread cutaneous and restricted visceral leishmaniasis, widespread schistosomiasis (*mansoni*), widespread Chagas disease, widespread malaria.

North Africa and Asia excluding India and S.E. Asia
Widespread dengue, guinea worm, some bancroftian filariasis, widespread cutaneous and restricted visceral leishmaniasis, restricted schistosomiasis, malaria.

India, S.E. Asia, the Indonesian and Philippine archipelago and Indian Ocean
Widespread dengue, guinea worm, widespread bancroftian and brugian filariasis, some cutaneous and more visceral leishmaniasis, restricted schistosomiasis (*japonicum*), widespread malaria, Japanese encephalitis.

New Guinea, Solomons, Vanuatu and other Islands of the Western Pacific
Restricted dengue, widespread bancroftian filariasis, restricted schistosomiasis (*japonicum*), widespread malaria.

Africa South of the Sahara, Madagascar and S.W. Arabia.
Widespread dengue and yellow fever, bancroftian filariasis, loiasis, widespread onchocerciasis, restricted cutaneous and visceral leishmaniasis, widespread schistosomiasis, sleeping sickness, widespread malaria, guinea worm.

likely. The accompanying series of world maps indicate the distribution of disease more accurately. Table 2-2 provides an alternative view of the association between disease and region. For detailed

Table 2-2

A broad indication of the distribution of disease between regions.

Japanese encephalitis is associated with rice growing and pig keeping in Asia, sometimes becoming more severe away from the equator.

Yellow fever is found in West Africa and South America, but not in Asia (although the vector is present).

Malaria is widespread in the tropics and sub-tropics, restricted by altitude.

Sleeping sickness is restricted to Africa, between the Sahara and the Zambezi river basin.

American trypanosomiasis, or Chagas disease, is restricted to Mexico, Central and South America. It is not specifically associated with water.

Bancroftian and brugian filariasis are associated with the humid tropics or coastal areas.

Onchocerciasis is restricted to West Africa, South and Central America and a few foci in East and Central Africa.

Dengue fever is spreading throughout the tropics and sub-tropics.

Dengue haemorrhagic fever is currently reported mainly from India, S.E. Asia, Philippines, the Caribbean and the Indian Ocean.

Schistosomiasis due to *S. mansoni* and *S. haematobium* is associated with the savannahs and semi-arid regions of Africa and the Middle-East and South America.

Schistosomiasis due to *S. japonicum* is restricted to South East Asia, China and the Philippines.

Other forms of schistosomiasis with very restricted distribution include *intercalatum* in Africa and *malayiensis/mekongi* in South East Asia.

information about insect vector distribution see WHO (1989); for schistosomiasis see Doumenge *et al.* (1987).

Map 1. Assessment of the global distribution of malaria, WHO (1987).

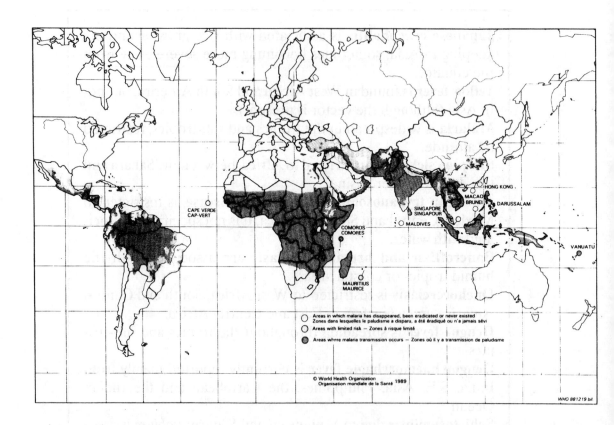

- ○ Areas in which malaria has disappeared, been eradicated or never existed
  Zones dans lesquelles le paludisme a disparu, a été éradiqué ou n'a jamais sévi
- ○ Areas with limited risk – Zones à risque limité
- ● Areas where malaria transmission occurs – Zones où il y a transmission de paludisme

© World Health Organization
Organisation mondiale de la Santé 1989

WHO 881219 bil.

Habitat

Vectors and vector-borne diseases are not distributed uniformly though a geographical region. They occur in relatively discrete patches where the habitat and climate are favourable. Table 2-3 indicates the principal habitats of the vectors or intermediate hosts associated with each of the principal diseases. It should be recognised that a development project will alter the environment and may create a habitat which was not previously present. If a disease occurs within the region and a habitat is created for the vector then, sooner or later, the habitat will be invaded and transmission may occur.

Table 2-3
The principal diseases associated with water in relation to the principal habitats
of the vectors.

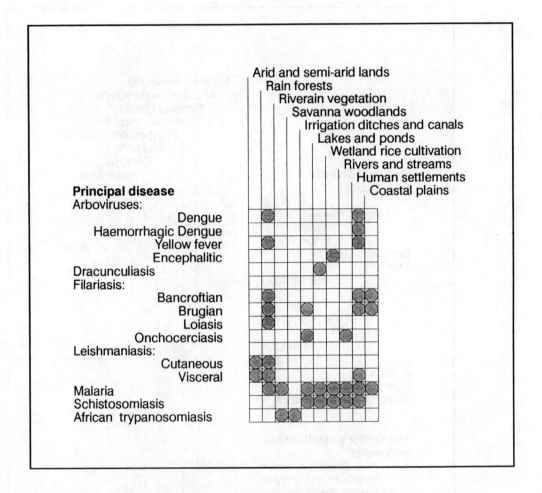

How The Diseases Are Transmitted

Vector-borne diseases may be categorised as water-based or water-related. In all cases the parasite or pathogen leaves an avian[1] or a mammalian host and must then undergo development in an insect, crustacean[2] or snail before entering a new avian or mammalian host. Environmental health engineering seeks to modify the environment in such a way as to eliminate suitable vector habitats and thus prevent or reduce the transmission. Table 2-4 explains the vector's relation-

1   Bird.
2   A class of mainly aquatic animals including crabs and shrimps

Table 2-4
Association between vector, disease and water.

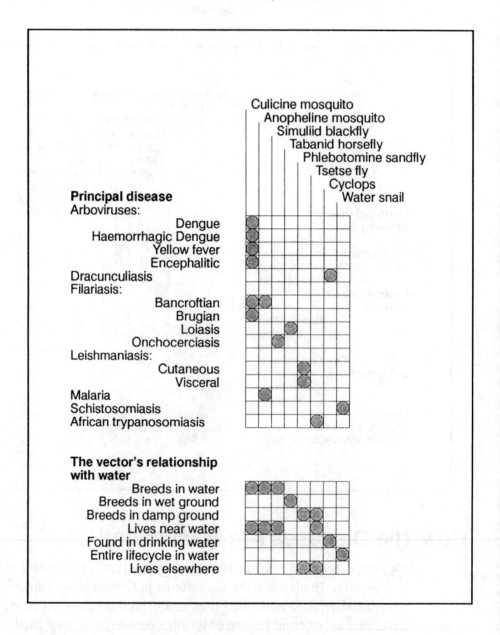

ship with water. Table 2-5 indicates which parasites have non-human animal hosts.

African trypanosomiasis (sleeping sickness) has been separated into Gambian, which is chronic and mainly West African, and Rhodesian,

Table 2-5
The main animal hosts of vector-borne diseases.

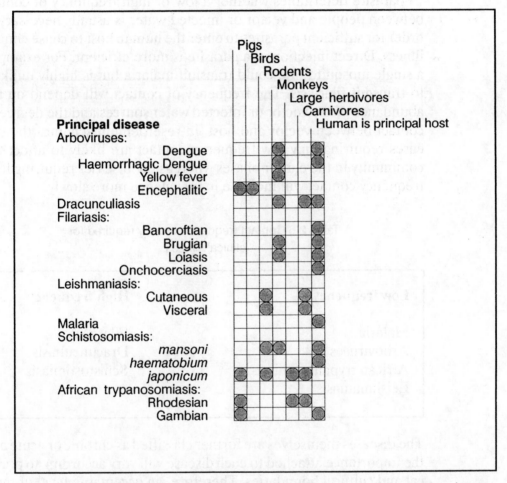

which is acute and mainly East African. Diseases with a predominantly animal reservoir are referred to as zoonoses. In the case of biting insects, transmission is further categorised according to whether the parasite is injected into the host (malaria, leishmaniasis, arboviruses, trypanosomiasis) or escapes from the insects mouthparts while blood-feeding (filariasis). The infective stage of schistosomiasis is released from an aquatic snail into water and penetrates the skin of a person in contact with the water. Dracunculiasis is transmitted by ingesting the tiny free swimming crustacean called *Cyclops*.

Contact Frequency

The method of transmission together with the life cycle of the parasite determines whether a low or high frequency of contact between people and vector or infected water is usually necessary in order for sufficient parasites to enter the human host to cause clinical illness. Direct injection of a parasite is more efficient. For example, a single mosquito bite could transmit malaria but is highly unlikely to transmit filariasis. The frequency of contact will depend on the abundance of the vector or infected water sources and the degree of contact between vector and host. In resettlement schemes the diseases requiring only low frequency contact are likely to affect the community in the earlier phases whereas the diseases requiring high frequency contact will increase in prevalence more slowly.

Table 2-6 Contact frequency usually required for
clinical illness.

Low frequency	High frequency
Malaria	Filariasis
Arboviruses	Dracunculiasis
African trypanosomiasis	Schistosomiasis
Leishmaniasis	

The diseases themselves are further classified as chronic or acute and the importance attached to each disease will vary according to political and cultural boundaries. Therefore, an acceptable level of morbidity or mortality will be determined by the national Ministry of Health. For example, the clinical gravity and socio-economic impact of schistosomiasis depends on the frequency of re-infection which depends, in turn, on the prevalence of the disease and the intensity of infection.

Mosquitoes

Mosquitoes are by far the most important family of insect vectors. W.H.O. (1982) contains a detailed description of their biology, importance and control. Mosquitoes are divided into two groups called anophelines and culicines.

The anophelines contain one important genus[1] called *Anopheles*. The culicines contain three important genera called *Culex*, *Aedes* and *Mansonia*. See Table 2-7. Note that only anophelines can transmit malaria, but not all anophelines do so. Table 1-5 indicated the flight range of each group.

Table 2-7
Distribution of mosquito-borne diseases.

Mosquito	Disease	Distribution
Subfamily: Anopheline Genus: *Anopheles*	Malaria	Throughout tropics and sub-tropics
	Bancroftian filariasis	Asia and Africa
	Brugian filariasis	Asia
	O'nyong nyong virus	Africa
Subfamily: Culicine Genus: *Culex*	Bancroftian filariasis	Throughout tropics
	Encephalitis virus	Asia, Americas, Europe, Africa
Subfamily: Culicine Genus: *Mansonia*	Brugian filariasis	Asia
	Other arboviruses	Africa, Americas
Subfamily: Culicine Genus: *Aedes*	Yellow fever virus	Africa, Americas
	Dengue virus	Asia, Americas, Africa
	Dengue Haemorragic	Asia , Americas
	Other arboviruses	Asia, Americas, Africa
	Bancroftian filariasis	Pacific

In common with other vectors, mosquitoes acquire the disease organism when feeding on an infected host and pass it to another host during a subsequent bloodmeal. The time taken for the organism to develop in the mosquito is temperature dependent, usually 10-17

---

1   Genus, genera: a sub-group consisting of similar or related species.

days. Only the female sucks blood and she does so to mature a batch of eggs. Each bloodmeal is followed by egg laying and the cycle takes 2-4 days. The cycle is repeated until the female dies. There are some 3000 species of mosquitoes of which about 100 are of medical importance. Mosquitoes are well adapted to capitalize on the environmental changes produced by water resource developments.

Breeding sites vary between species

Mosquito eggs are deposited in water. The type of water preferred varies between species. Preferred sites include small containers, edges of reservoirs, sunlit rainpools, shaded water and foul water. The type of vegetation in the water is also important. Eggs hatch within days and the aquatic larvae feed on microorganisms. They are capable of rapid wriggling movements. They must come to the surface to breathe, except for the larvae of the *Mansonia* mosquito. A layer of oil on water prevents many species from breathing. *Mansonia* extracts oxygen from aquatic plants and does not come to the surface to breathe. It can be controlled by removing certain species of plants. The larval stage of all tropical mosquitoes lasts 5-10 days. The pupal stage wriggles and breathes but does not feed. The pupal stage lasts 1-2 days. After emergence the female only mates once during her life. Feeding habits vary considerably between species with respect to time, place and host preference. The preference for blood of a particular group of animals such as birds, bovids (cows) or pigs determines the degree of feeding on humans and the likelihood of acquiring a disease organism from an animal reservoir. Malaria and bancroftian filariasis do not have animal reservoirs and only mosquitoes with a high preference for human blood are important for disease transmission. For mosquitoes with a less pronounced preference, large numbers of domestic animals may act as diversionary hosts and this can be used in control strategies by placing domestic animals between breeding sites and human habitations [1]. The viruses often have animal reservoirs and are transmitted by species which prefer animal blood but which occasionally bite people. Irrigation schemes may attract such animal reservoirs to areas where there is closer contact with mosquitoes which are also biting people. The blood preference does not change but the availability of host species has changed.

---

1   Zooprophylaxis

Where and when a mosquito bites and where it rests after biting also has a great impact on disease transmission. Many important species feed indoors and rest indoors after feeding, making them potentially vulnerable to residual insecticides sprayed on in-house surfaces. Malaria and filariasis vectors usually bite at night and hence individuals sleeping without mosquito netting, or outside their houses, are at risk. Many of the arbovirus infections are transmitted by outdoor, daytime biting mosquitoes.

General Mosquito Control Methods

The available methods of mosquito control are usually classified as chemical, biological and environmental. Chemical and environmental control may be directed at either the adults or the larvae whereas biological control is directed at the larvae. Chemical control methods are apparently very powerful. However, they are subject to the following main limitations.

- All insects eventually develop resistance to all practical chemical insecticides. The supply of new insecticides is limited.
- People object to having their homes sprayed with chemicals for a variety of reasons.

Chemical control of adult mosquitoes may be designed either to reduce abundance or to reduce the risk of parasite transmission. The chemicals are sprayed in or around peoples' homes. Attempts to reduce abundance involve space spraying and fogging and are only temporarily effective. Residual spraying involves applying insecticides with a persistent effect to all surfaces where mosquitoes are likely to rest. The residual effect may last from a few weeks to over a year. Residual spraying reduces the risk of parasite transmission by reducing mosquito longevity rather than abundance. It has been very effective at interrupting malaria transmission but only when the vector species rests on a relatively small number of surfaces which are clearly defined and accessible. For example, they may rest on cool, dark walls inside houses. Chemicals are also used as repellents and may be vaporised, as in mosquito coils, or impregnated in clothing and netting.

Chemical control of larvae (larviciding) involves spraying chemicals on a substantial proportion of the breeding sites in the environment. The residual effect is usually more limited and lasts for less than a week. Larviciding is effective at reducing adult abundance when there are relatively few breeding sites and they are clearly defined and accessible. For example, some mosquitoes breed in liquid sullage and sewage associated with human communities.

Biological control consists of introducing or encouraging the predators and parasites of mosquito larvae. For example, *Gambusia* fish are voracious predators of mosquito larvae. If the population of the control agent can be maintained at sufficiently high numbers then the vector population may be substantially reduced. However, it is generally necessary to reintroduce the control agent at intervals of a few weeks to a few years.

Environmental management consists of reducing the number and size of mosquito breeding sites and the frequency of contact between people and vectors. Mosquito breeding sites may be destroyed by measures such as draining, filling low lying areas, removing shade vegetation and fitting tight lids to water containers. Contact may be reduced by land-use zoning or screening houses and beds.

Anopheline Mosquitoes

M any anophelines transmit malaria and filariasis but they are less important than other mosquitoes in the transmission of arboviruses. Within any one geographical area, usually only 2-3 species are of major medical importance and there will usually be important differences in their breeding sites and behaviour. Generally, anophelines breed in all kinds of relatively unpolluted water.

Environmental Control Methods For Anophelines

Appropriate control methods vary according to the class of breeding site. The following are examples.

- Anopheline mosquitoes may breed in isolated pools associated with impoundments and rivers in which the the water level fluctuates. The shore line may be altered so as to minimise indentations, optimise bank slopes and remove vegetation. Fluctuations in water level can be controlled by manipulation of storage reservoirs.

- Anopheline mosquitoes may breed among emergent vegetation at the edges of impoundments and ditches where the larvae are protected from currents or wave action. The banks should be regularly cleared of vegetation and a proper gradient maintained.

- Anopheline mosquitoes may breed in rice fields where mosquito productivity changes markedly with the height of the rice plants. See

FAO (1984) and IRRI/PEEM (1989). Control methods include intermittent irrigation, stocking with larvivorous fishes and siting villages several kilometres away from the rice fields.

- Anopheline mosquitoes may breed in temporary rainpools which are widely scattered throughout the environment and impossible to remove. However, such breeding sites may be very seasonal. Control consists of the seasonal use of screens and residual insecticides.

- In urban areas anophelines usually breed in artificial water containers such as cisterns, wells, metal drums, overhead tanks and ornamental ponds. Breeding is controlled by emptying containers every few days, fitting tight lids or introducing larvivorous fishes.

Culicine Mosquitoes: Genus Culex

Culex mosquitoes play an important role in the transmission of a number of virus infections, many of which originate in birds. Throughout tropical Asia, India and Japan a dominant ricefield breeding *Culex* mosquito is the principal vector of Japanese ence-

Map 2. Assessment of the global distribution of human lymphatic filariasis in the major endemic zones, WHO (1987).

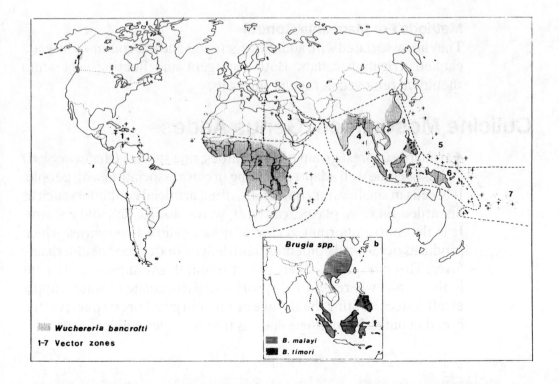

Wuchereria bancrofti

1-7 Vector zones

Brugia spp.

B. *malayi*
B. *timori*

phalitis virus. This serious viral disease can easily be promoted by water resource development, especially when large numbers of pigs are reared nearby. See IRRI/PEEM (1989).

The common urban *Culex* mosquito breeds in foul water such as latrines, blocked drains and septic pools. Rapid urbanization without provision for waste disposal promotes large populations of this species. In many places it transmits bancroftian filariasis.

Methods For Culex Control

Rice field breeding *Culex* are controlled in the same way as anophelines. The common urban species may easily be controlled by proper urban sanitation including the provision of well designed drains, sealed septic tanks or latrines and solid waste disposal. The operation and maintenance of urban sanitation and drainage systems requires constant vigilance.

Culicine Mosquitoes: Genus Mansonia

The *Mansonia* mosquitoes are relatively unimportant for virus transmission. Their role as a vector is restricted to rural areas in Asia where they transmit brugian filariasis. In many placse they are a major biting nuisance by day and night.

Methods For Mansonia Control

They are associated with aquatic vegetation and are common in weed choked irrigation canals. Both emergent and floating vegetation should be removed at regular intervals.

Culicine Mosquitoes: Genus Aedes

Primarily a forest group of mosquitoes, one species (*Aedes aegypti*) has become well adapted to living in close association with people. It breeds in small water collections, often artificial containers such as discarded tin cans, plastic, car tyres, water storage jars and cisterns. It is the most important vector of urban yellow fever virus, which produces occasional epidemics, and dengue or dengue haemorrhagic fever. This mosquito is likely to be present in any human settlement in the tropics where refuse disposal is indiscriminate or water supply erratic - necessitating the storage of water in jars. Forest species often breed in natural containers such as tree rot holes and leaf axils.

Methods For Aedes Control

Solid waste, especially containers, must be collected and removed. Water storage jars and cisterns should be fitted with lids. Ornamental water containers and ant traps should be emptied often. Gutters should be kept clean and functional. Special attention should be paid to the storage of potential containers. For example, used car tyre dumps are well-known breeding foci. Piped water supplies may be improved. Villages may be sited several kilometres away from forest edges.

Effect Of Irrigation And Dams On Mosquito Breeding

Hydrological changes following irrigation development or dam construction may lead to a significant increase in the extent of mosquito breeding sites and in their seasonal duration. Thus seasonal transmission of a disease such as malaria may be extended. It should be emphasised that each species has its own peculiar biology and environmental requirements and therefore the detailed design of a water development project should take account of the attributes of local vector species.

Mosquitoes which normally breed in small collections of water, such as *Anopheles gambiae* in Africa, may decrease in numbers as their numerous, separate habitats are submerged. On the other hand the shallow shoreline of a large water body may provide extensive new breeding sites. The shallows become invaded by weeds and aquatic vegetation which provide refuges against waves, wind and current action and from predators.

Deep reservoirs with regular shorelines and steeply sloped margins have a low marsh potential and are likely to support far less mosquito breeding than shallow reservoirs with a long, irregular shoreline and gently sloped margins.

Wave-wash and surface agitation reduce mosquito (and snail) breeding and measures to increase them may be helpful. On clay soils wave action may help to preserve the bank profile and increase turbidity. Peripheral vegetation may require clearing, particularly close to settlements. In Africa, clearing riverine and lacustrine vegetation is an important measure in reducing contact between people and tsetse flies; for this purpose cleared strips must be of adequate size, since small clearings may actually serve as tsetse feeding sites.

The higher the marsh potential the further away should human settlements be sited. Inadequate clearing of vegetation during construction may result in the accumulation of floating debris in inlets, the growth of aquatic vegetation and mosquito breeding. Systematic fluctuation in the water level can do much to reduce vector breeding by stranding eggs, larvae and pupae. However, if temporary pools are created at the margins then other important mosquito vectors may be encouraged to breed.

Night storage dams pose a particular problem

Night storage dams pose a particular problem for disease control. During periods of irrigation, 24hr cycles of filling and emptying will normally deter vectors. Outside the main growing period the water level may stabilise and emergent vegetation and pool formation may encourage breeding.

Rivers and streams can provide breeding sites for mosquitoes as dry season rock pools and as flood pools in low lying basins. Flash floods are significant features of tropical rivers and may flush larvae out of rock pools but recharge flood pools. Gabions, levees or dykes may help prevent flood pools. Sluicing and flushing by automatic syphons or hand-operated gates is often effective in preventing breeding in streams and canals.

Mosquitoes flourish in irrigation systems where there are badly designed or maintained feeder canals, smaller canals and ditches. The risk is greatest where debris and silt are allowed to accumulate and vegetation to flourish. Changes in direction, gradient and velocity may result in regions of sluggish flow where mosquitoes can breed. Vegetation may support *Mansonia* mosquitoes. Excessive seepage and overflow may produce water collections.

Mosquito production on irrigated land is directly related to the extent and duration of flooding of the inundated area. Alternate wetting and drying, a form of intermittent irrigation, deters mosquito breeding. The more sophisticated the method of irrigation the less likely it is to encourage mosquito breeding. Thus, uncontrolled flooding with little drainage presents the greatest risk; piped water, for sprinkler or drip irrigation, presents the least risk.

Simuliid Blackflies

There are many species of blackflies, the most important belong to the *Simulium damnosum* complex[1] which is the vector of river blindness or onchocerciasis over most of Africa between 13°N and 13°S. There are other vector species in Africa and yet more in South and Central America.

Simuliids lay their eggs in flowing water. The aquatic larvae and pupae attach firmly to the substrate, even in violently turbulent rapids. The larvae feed by filtering selectively sized particles out of the moving water. The larval stage lasts 5-10 days. The adult female fly requires blood to mature her egg batch, much like mosquitoes. They feed by day in the vicinity of the breeding site but may fly 5km in search of a suitable host. A bloodmeal is required every 4-5 days. Rivers often dry up during the dry season, but reinvasion by blackflies frequently occurs from remote parts, as some species are able to

Map 3. Geographical distribution of river blindness or onchocerciasis in Africa and the Arabian Peninsula , WHO (1986).

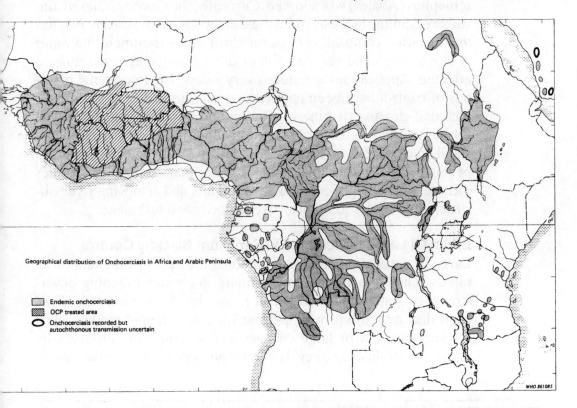

Geographical distribution of Onchocerciasis in Africa and Arabic Peninsula

- Endemic onchocerciasis
- OCP treated area
- Onchocerciasis recorded but autochthonous transmission uncertain

WHO 861085

---

1   A group of species previously considered a single species.

migrate distances of more than 400km when aided by the prevailing wind.

They pick up the parasite *Onchocerca volvulus* when feeding on an infected person. There is no known animal reservoir. They transmit the parasite at a subsequent bloodmeal. The parasite takes about 18 months to mature in the human host and then lives and reproduces for more than 10 years.

Methods Of Controlling River Blindness Transmission

Until recently, there were no satisfactory drugs for treating the disease or killing the worms in the human body. A new drug called Ivermectin is currently under trial. Present methods of control, however, concentrate on killing the vector to prevent transmission. Since the larvae are sessile[1] and limited to the fastest parts of rivers they are the easiest stage to attack. Very low concentrations of insecticide are added to the river water at these foci. The insecticide is carried down-stream by the river flow and kills all larvae over several kms. Earlier chemical control schemes used DDT at 0.5ppm/30 min. Later temephos (Abate®) was adopted. Currently, the Onchocerciasis Control Programme in West Africa uses temephos, chlorphoxim, *Bacillus thuringiensis*[2], carbosulfan or permethrin. After treatment the water is safe to drink and very few fish or other non-target organisms are affected. Applications are made every 7 days. Environmental methods of control have been applied to a very limited extent and have included clearing riverine vegetation and water management. The former method was effective for controlling *Simulium neavei* on one small river system in Kenya. The larvae of this species have the peculiar habit of attaching to crabs. Water management techniques include controlling the spillage from dams and removing river obstructions in order to reduce water velocity and turbulence.

Effect Of Large Structures On Simulium Blackfly Control

Large projects often eliminate breeding upstream by inundation of rapids. They may reduce or eliminate low water breeding downstream by stabilising discharge at higher levels than normal. However, they may also provide permanent downstream breeding sites. Intermittent flow or large changes in discharge can kill larvae by drying out or flushing away. It may be possible to incorporate insec-

---

1   Attached to the river bed
2   A naturally occuring bacterium which kills some types of insects

ticide injection systems into discharge pipes or to regulate flow over alternate spillways.

All spillway structures provide potential breeding sites. Some spillway designs cause massive breeding in an area where breeding was previously absent or slight.

Effect Of Small Structures On Simulium Blackfly Control

Provision of adequate water supplies may reduce the contact which a community has with the river bank, where most biting occurs. There are few other advantages.

Such projects may encourage breeding in areas where it did not exist before. Poor spillway design may provide excellent breeding sites. Downstream scouring of river beds may expose rock which forms a suitable breeding substrate. The periods of flow in normally intermittent streams may be increased. Small dam outlets are very difficult to treat with insecticides.

The disadvantages can be minimised by thoughtful design. Structures must be strong enough to avoid leaks and fractures. Inclined planes on spillways must be avoided. Vertical or over-hung spillways are best. Discharge into deep still pools or into smooth channels with low water velocity is preferred. Perforated pipes for insecticide application can be incorporated during the construction phase.

Phlebotomine Sandflies

The term sandfly is applied to two quite different groups of biting flies. The ceratopogonid sandflies are minute midges (< 1mm) which often occur in enormous numbers. They are a nuisance but not important for human disease transmission.

The phlebotomine sandflies are a little larger (1-4mm). They hold their wings in a V above their backs and make short hopping flights. They are usually active in dark places or at night. They are important vectors of all forms of leishmaniasis. They also transmit a virus causing sandfly fever and a bacterium causing Oroya fever which is restricted to a few Andean valleys. Some people react violently to sandfly bites.

Unlike most other biting flies, sandflies avoid free water. Their eggs are laid on damp surfaces and their larvae require a humid atmosphere in which they browse on decaying organic matter. Little is known of the precise breeding site requirements of sandflies. They breed in deep cracks in the ground, in rodent burrows, termite hills, organic debris in tree holes or in the leaf litter of S. American forest floors.

Most important Old World species live in arid or semi-arid areas in close association with the desert rodents on which they normally feed. These areas are commonly highly attractive for irrigation projects which have brought large numbers of labourers followed by settlers into previously uninhabited areas and exposed them to the bite of sandflies and thus to infection with leishaniasis. In addition, some species of sandflies live in close association with human settlements and feed on people or domestic animals.

Colonial desert rodents create habitats

The colonial desert rodents, *Meriones* species, *Rhombomys opimus* and *Psammomys obesus* create ideal habitats for sandflies (in their relatively cool, moist burrows) across the entire Old World arid belt, from the northern edge of the Sahara desert to Mongolia and northern India. These animals provide a reservoir of leishmaniasis. Habitats suitable for the rodents are usually in low lying areas with deep friable alluvial or loess soils which lack only water before becoming highly productive.

Agricultural development associated with water development affects the sandflies in two main ways. Ploughing and other land disturbances eliminate *Rhombomys* or *Psammomys* which are the two main reservoir hosts of cutaneous leishmaniasis, but often encourage *Merionnes* to increase in numbers and therefore become more important. The second effect comes with the raising of the water table which encourages a sandfly species which is the most efficient vector of rural cutaneous leishmaniasis.

Serious outbreaks of cutaneous leishmaniasis associated with water development projects have been reported from Libya, Saudi Arabia, USSR, Pakistan and India. In USSR participation of public health engineers and landscape epidemiology teams in water development has led to effective control and prevented outbreaks amongst labourers and settlers.

In the New World, the vectors and the reservoirs are most abundant in primary and secondary forest. Exposure to leishmaniasis is the result of intrusion into the forest and has no specific connection with water development. Forest destruction eliminates the cutaneous

leishmaniasis vectors but encourages the vector of visceral leishmaniasis.

Phlebotomine Sandfly Control

Most phlebotomine sandflies are very susceptible to insecticides and
urban populations have been controlled as a by-product of malaria
control campaigns using residual sprays. However, most control
campaigns have concentrated on the rodent or canine hosts. Colonies
of wild rodents have been destroyed by poisoning or bulldozing prior
to agricultural land development.

Tsetse Flies

Tsetse flies, or *Glossina*, are large, stout flies with a painful bite that
are only found in Sub-saharan Africa (15°N to 20°S, extending to
30°S on the eastern seaboard). They transmit African trypanosomiasis to people (sleeping sickness) and livestock (nagana). Tsetse
feed on a wide range of mammals, birds and reptiles. Adults rest on
shaded trees and hunt by site on open ground, often following vehicles. They seldom venture far into open spaces and a clearing of 0.5
- 4.0 km is often an effective barrier. Contrary to other insect species,
they do not lay eggs but give birth to live young which burrow into
damp shaded patches of soil or leaf litter, where they become pupae
and change into adult flies.

Broadly speaking, West African tsetse feed on people and reptiles,
inhabit lacustrine or riverine woodlands and transmit gambian sleeping sickness which is not a zoonosis. There are foci of infection at
wooded river crossings, water holes and lake shores. East African
tsetse feed mainly on wild animals, inhabit dry savanna woodlands,
forestry plantations, thickets and hedges and transmit rhodesian
sleeping sickness which is a zoonosis. The bushbuck is an important
host of tsetse and a reservoir of rhodesian sleeping sickness.

Control Methods

Tsetse are controlled by selective application of insecticides, traps or
bush clearance. Wholesale bush clearance is effective but harmful to
the environment. Selective and partial bush clearance involves removal of specific shade trees, undergrowth or creation of clearings which
tsetse cannot cross. Tsetse populations are often diminished by water
development but sleeping sickness remains a problem where groups
of people venture into wooded areas. As epidemics can occur rapidly

Map 4. Principal foci of sleeping sickness in Africa, WHO (1985).

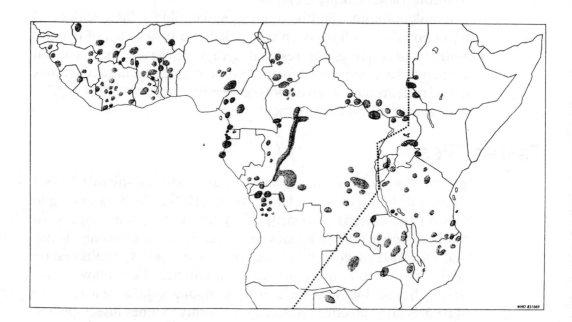

WHO 851669

there is a need for constant vigilance. Chemoprophylaxis can be provided for groups such as construction workers.

Tabanids, Horseflies, Deerflies

Tabanids, also known as horseflies or deerflies, are large, stout flies with a painful bite. Members of the genus *Chrysops* transmit a filarial nematode which causes loasis. Loasis is found in Central and West Africa. The disease is characterised by transient cutaneous swellings.

Tabanids breed in the mud and decaying vegetation of forest swamps. The adults are active by day, often in bright sunshine. Larval control is difficult and includes clearing shade vegetation and draining swamps. Personal protection against bites can be affected by screening houses, wearing long trousers and using repellents.

Cyclops

These are tiny free swimming creatures which contaminate fresh water. Several species are intermediate hosts of the worm which causes dracunculiasis. *Cyclops* may swallow the eggs of the parasite which then develop in the body cavity. When people swallow infected *Cyclops*, the larvae are released and migrate through the human body. The gravid female parasites usually live in the skin of the legs and feet, under a blister. When in contact with water the eggs of the parasite are released and contaminate the water. Chronic[1] infection causes ulceration[2].

Control Methods

Transmission occurs where drinking water is drawn from shallow wells or ponds into which people wade to fill their containers. *Cyclops* live in stagnant water with a high organic content. Control may be obtained by protecting drinking water, sieving contaminated water or killing *Cyclops* with a safe insecticide such as temephos (Abate ®).

Snails And Schistosomiasis (Bilharzia)

The three principal forms of schistosomiasis are listed in table 2-8 but there are other forms with restricted foci. The parasites lodge in the veins of either the intestines or the urinary tract and the eggs are passed in either the faeces or urine. The eggs hatch in water and the mobile larva (miracidium) seeks out and enters the aquatic snail. Multiplication takes place and the infective stage (cerceriae) are

Table 2-8
The principal genera of snails and the principal form of schistosomiasis (bilharzia) which they transmit.

Snail genus	Parasite	Type of Disease
Oncomelania	*S. japonicum*	Intestinal
Biomphalaria	*S. mansoni*	Intestinal
Bulinus	*S. haematobium*	Urinary

---

1   Long term
2   Deep, open sores

Map 5. Global distribution of schistosomiasis due to *S. mansoni* and *S. intercalatum*, WHO (1985).

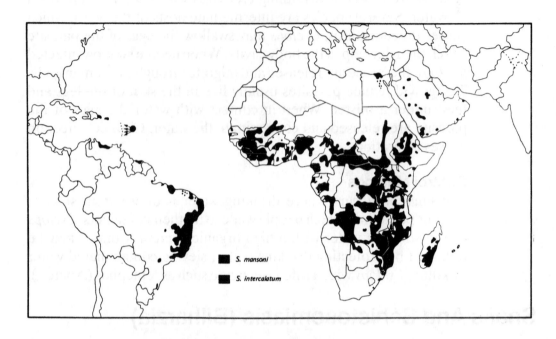

Map 6. Global distribution of schistosomiasis due to *S. haematobium* and *S. japonicum*, WHO (1985).

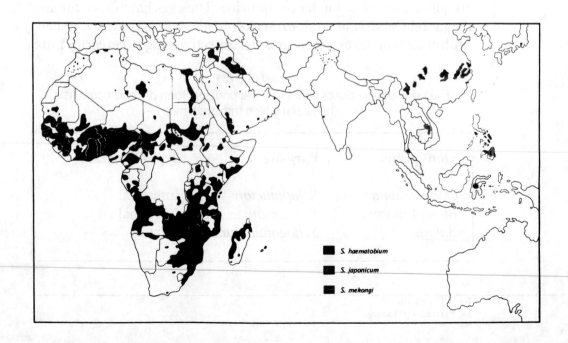

emitted after about 3-8 weeks. The snail may survive and remain infective for upto 6 months. The free swimming cerceriae are active in the water for 12-48 hours during which time they can penetrate the skin of a person who enters the water and cause infection. Cercerial emission is stimulated by warmth and light and usually occurs between 10 am and 2 pm, peaking at noon - the most dangerous times to enter unsafe water.

Each of the three genera of snails contains many species and each species contains many strains which vary in their susceptibility to the parasite. A particular water body could contain different species of snails, only some of which are important.

Snail Habitats

Oncomelanian snails are amphibious and can be found in considerable numbers on wet ground, the others are not. Some species of snails can survive the drying up of temporary pools by hiding in the mud. *Biomphalaria* snails like stable, slowly flowing water and are dominant in long established water bodies. *Bulinus* like unstable, semi-stagnant water and colonise newly inundated water bodies. Other favourable conditions for snails are listed in table 2-9.

Table 2-9
List of favourable habitat requirements for aquatic snails (*Bulinus* and *Biomphalaria*)

Moderate light penetration	Gradient < 20m/km
Little turbidity	Temperature 0-37°C
Partial shade	Optimal temperature 18-28°C
Water velocity < 0.3m/s	Firm mud substrate
Slight pollution with excreta	Gradual change in water level

Snail Control

Snails may be controlled by chemicals, biological agents or environmental engineering. Synthetic molluscicides are effective but very expensive and may kill fishes. Natural molluscicides, from plant extracts, and biological agents (such as competitive snails) are not fully developed. Engineering methods of snail control are most important and should be incorporated at the project design stage. Some of the most important are listed in table 2-10.

Water Contact

People come into contact with unsafe water through three broad categories of activity.

- Recreation, such as swimming.
- Occupation, such as irrigation, fishing and crossing water.
- Domestic, such as fetching water, washing clothes and bathing.

The water is made unsafe by pollution with human excreta. This occurs through ignorance, overcrowding, indiscriminant urination and defecation and poor siting of settlements. Children, especially teenage males, are the principal sources of infection because of the desire to bathe and play.

Table 2-10
List of principal engineering methods for vector control. See WHO (1982) for further details.

CANAL DESIGN
Straight canals to eliminate standing pools.
Mechanical screening of water intakes against snails. Bridged crossing points.
Built-in chemical dispensers at strategic points.
Vegetation clearance.
Seepage control.

RESERVOIR DESIGN
Minimum night storage reservoirs.
Periodic drawdown.
Vegetation clearance.
Spillways. Inundation of breeding sites. Steep, regular banks.

IRRIGATION AND DRAINAGE DESIGN
Increase water velocity, but prevent scouring.
Desilting and vegetation clearance to prevent slow water flow and to remove food for snails.
Proper field drainage.

Maintenance of field drains.
Lining major water contact points.
Sprinkler irrigation if feasible.
Filling surface water collections.
Intermittent irrigation.

SETTLEMENT DESIGN
Properly sited villages.
Piped water supplies.
Properly designed and located latrines to ensure effective use and to prevent sewage entering water system.
Fencing and zoning. Pathways and bridges.
Children's swimming pools and other recreation sites.
Communal laundries. Waste disposal.
Home construction materials and design.
Domestic animal pens.

EARTHWORKS
Diking, drainage, grading and infilling.

Control Of Schistosomiasis

Schistosomiasis may be controlled by treatment, reduction of water contact, reduction of contamination by health education and sanitation and by removing snails. Treatment is beneficial to individuals, particularly those who are heavily infected, by reducing the risk of developing severe chronic diseases. However, the long term effect on transmission will be minimal if neither the entire population is treated nor the health service infrastructure able to provide periodic examination and treatment. The cost of treatment is constantly decreasing so that health services can contribute to control with minimal hard currency support.

Reduction in water contact is best achieved by the availability of alternative water supplies for domestic needs. Prevention of water contact is difficult especially among children. Health education should be directed towards:

- changing people's understanding of their role in causing schistosomiasis by poor hygiene;
- encouraging people to change their habits of defecation and urination;
- promoting self-help groups to construct water supply and sanitation facilities.

The cost of water supply and sanitation is relatively inexpensive in relation to overall development costs and will benefit the health of the community as well as the workers. Siting settlements more than 2km from irrigation systems can be effective if adequate sanitation facilities are maintained within the irrigation system. Informal, peripheral housing is usually unplanned with inadequate sanitation, poor drainage and stagnant water bodies. It is an important transmission site. Bridges at major crossing points, fencing and provision of recreational swimming facilities are all effective methods of avoiding contact with contaminated water if adequately maintained.

Safeguards And Mitigation Measures

Safeguards are interventions which are intended to prevent health hazards from developing. In contrast, mitigation measures are interventions which are intended to make health hazards less severe. The decision-maker will always be faced with a choice between alternative interventions, including the choice of doing nothing. Therefore, there will always be a need to summarise the beneficial and detrimental effects of interventions, their relative costs and their effect on non-health related factors, such as agricultural productivity.

Whose Responsibility Is Health?

Experience has shown that the responsibility for the health component of a water development project oftens falls between different administrative structures. There is an urgent need for appropriate institutional arrangements in which responsibility for health is clearly defined. See Tiffen (1989).

When To Intervene

Design Phase

The obvious time to incorporate safeguards into a development project is during the design phase, before the health hazards have developed. A forecast of the vector-borne disease implications should be obtained for the case of no special safeguards and then for each alternative group of safeguards. The design of permanent structures will have the most long term impact on health. The health department should approve and countersign the plans before construction commences.

Construction Phase

During the construction phase special skills will be required and the work force will often be recruited by the engineering contractor. The health of the recruits and their immune status will determine whether construction proceeds in a smooth and timely fashion. The engineer may be responsible for the health of the work force and their families. An informal sector, squatters, may settle nearby and sell goods and services to the recruits and thereby affect their health. The contractor may screen his new employees and offer treatment.

Temporary accommodation on and off the worksite provides plenty of opportunity for vector breeding. The contractor may instigate control measures.

Operation Phase

During the operation phase the responsibility for health is likely to be transferred progressively to the health department. However, it takes time to train or redeploy personnel and to construct dispensaries and accommodation. Therefore, it is the planners responsi-

Figure 2-1 How development can affect health.

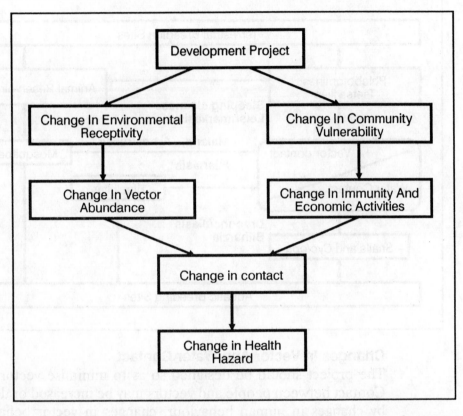

bility to communicate with the health department at an early stage. The managers of the project should remain responsible for maintenance and operating procedures which reduce health risks and be accountable to the health department.

Where To Intervene

Figure 2-1 illustrates the changes which may occur during a water development project. Intervention may be possible at any of these points. Figure 2-2 summarises the transmission pathways for several vector-borne diseases.

Figure 2-2
The pathways by which water resource development projects affect vector-borne disease transmission.

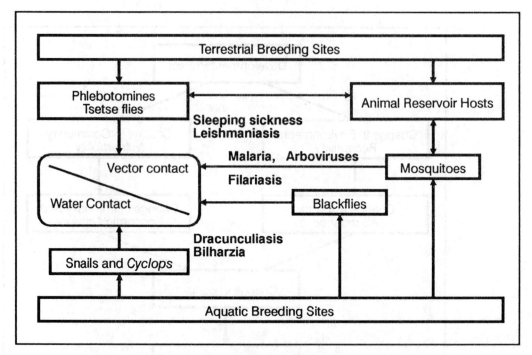

Changes In Vector And Water Contact

The project should be designed so as to minimise vector contact.
Contact between people and vectors may be increased or decreased
by changes in human behaviour, changes in vector behaviour or
changes in vector abundance. Each species of vector has preferred
locations and times for seeking a blood-meal. For example, human
contact with tsetse flies may occur when people venture into or near
relatively undisturbed woodlands during daylight. As another
example, contact with some species of mosquito may occur when
people are sleeping inside their houses during the night.

The project should be designed so as to minimise contact with unsafe
water. Contact between people and water containing intermediate
hosts may be increased or decreased by changes in human behaviour
or changes in abundance of the intermediate host. The infective stage
of schistosomiasis burrows into the skin of people who are bathing,
drinking or playing in water which is the breeding site of certain snail
species which, in turn, are the intermediate host. The water must first
have been polluted by the urine or faeces of infected people. Dracunculiasis may be contracted when infected water is drunk.

Changes In Terrestrial Breeding Sites

Changes in terrestrial habitats may affect the breeding sites and hence abundance of insect vectors or animal reservoir hosts. For example, phlebotomine sandflies breed in the burrows of certain species of rodents which may be reservoirs of the *Leishmania* parasite. The rodents favour certain kinds of topology, soil and vegetation. Similarly, tsetse fly breed in relatively moist and shaded patches of an otherwise hot and dry environment. Savannah tsetse feed on large game animals such as bushbuck which may be reservoirs of trypanosomes.

Changes In Aquatic Breeding Sites

Changes in aquatic habitats may affect the breeding sites and hence abundance of both intermediate hosts and insect vectors. For example, mosquitoes and simuliid blackflies both breed in water and transmit malaria and filariasis directly between people. Some species of mosquitoes also feed on birds or animals which may be reservoirs of arboviruses. Snails and *Cyclops*, the intermediate hosts of schistosomiasis and dracunculiasis, also breed in water.

Appropriate Interventions

Careful design of water development projects should help ensure that the abundance of important vector and host species is low and that human contact with vectors and infected water sources is minimised. The most appropriate interventions are multi-sectoral and have the following attributes.

- They reduce several health hazards simultaneously.

- They have a positive impact on other, non-health related, activities or problems. In this case the costs of implementation, which might otherwise not be affordable, may be shared. For example, the water management principles required to maintain economic productivity in irrigation systems also reduce the risk of schistosomiasis. These principles include measures to avoid erosion, sedimentation and water logging. The least appropriate interventions conflict with other objectives. In this case a trade-off would be necessary.

WHO (1982) have classified environmental measures into 3 primary groups.

Environmental modifications are large scale or permanent alterations to the environment aimed at preventing, eliminating or reduc-

Table 2-11
Examples of interventions which are designed to control vectors and the vector
groups which may be affected (WHO, 1980).

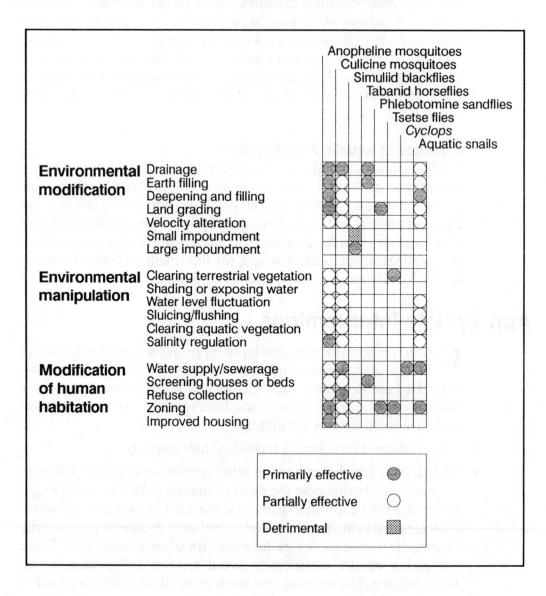

ing vector habitats. Although long-lasting, such works may still require proper operation and maintenance.

Environmental manipulations consist of any planned recurrent activity aimed at producing temporary conditions unfavourable to vector breeding sites or habitats.

Modification or manipulation of human habitation or behaviour is intended to reduce contact with vectors or unsafe water.

Table 2-11 illustrates some examples of these interventions and the groups of vectors on which they may have beneficial impact. Other examples of interventions are scattered throughout the document.

In summary, safeguards and mitigation measures consist of a judicious mixture of:

- High standards of design and construction.
- Maintenance.
- Siting.
- Appropriate and effective institutional arrangements which aim to integrate available control measures.

The other documents in this series should be consulted for further details.

Evaluating And Monitoring

One of the most important safeguards which can be incorporated into a water development project is an effective scheme for monitoring and evaluating the vector population, disease prevalence and control operation during every project phase.

Forecasting and decision-making processes require revision in the light of new information. However, monitoring must be selective as it requires scarce resources. The objective should be to provide relevant information. The catchword is "optimal ignorance". Monitoring should ideally be started during the feasibility study so that hard data, representing one whole year of baseline studies, is available before the design is finalised.

Evaluation and monitoring of health related factors is clearly the responsibility of the health department and emphasises, again, the need to establish intersectoral linkages.

Chapter 3

A summary of experience

Introduction

Specialist knowledge often depends on experience which may be summarised as rules-of-thumb, aphorisms or heuristics. These are approximations, valid when a combination of conditions are satisfied, which suggest a possible outcome to a series of events. In the following we have simplified these rules as though they were always true or false. In reality, the degree of certainty will depend on context. The results of a user survey indicated that this approach was especially useful for non-health specialists.

The experience is grouped under the following main headings.

- Geophysical such as rainfall, topology and water chemistry;
- Biotic, such as vegetation, animals and farming;
- Demographic and socio-cultural, such as customs and settlements;
- Infrastructure, including planning and management;
- Disease management by vector control.

A standard, logical formulation has been adopted based on the terms: *if*; *then*; *and*; *or*; and *not*. An extensive cross-referencing system is provided in the document index.

Geophysical

Season

If the climate is seasonal then vectors may vary in abundance through the year.

If malaria is stable then additional vectors may not affect the incidence of the disease significantly.

If there is a season during which vectors and snails are unable to breed then disease transmission may be interrupted during that season.

If the seasonal abundance of standing water is increased then the period of interrupted transmission is reduced.

If domestic animals such as cattle, buffaloes and pigs are seasonally abundant then they may divert vectors away from human hosts.

If a development project alters the abundance of domestic animals then the diversionary effect is altered.

If people sleep outside during hot weather then they may attract outdoor biting mosquitoes.

If there are seasonal food shortages then there may be a seasonal increase in susceptibility to infection.

If there is a water development scheme then seasonal food shortages may be reduced.

If there is increased contact with limited dry season water supplies then intense focal transmission of schistosomiasis may occur.

Temperature and Altitude

If the mean temperature is below 17°C then parasite development in the vector or intermediate host ceases (20°C for *falciparum* malaria, 14°C for schistosomiasis).

If the temperature is very high then parasite development ceases and the activity of vectors is reduced.

If a development project is planned at altitudes at which pathogen transmission is rare then the potential increase will be negligible.

Wind

If the project is in West Africa and there are blackfly vectors breeding within 400 km upwind then recolonization of seasonal streams may be expected.

If wind assists the drift of floatage then the dispersal of snail vectors may be increased.

If the site is generally windy then insect biting activity will be greatly reduced.

If there are exposed shores subject to wave action then the breeding of snails and mosquitoes will be greatly reduced.

Geophysical

Humidity

If the microclimate humidity is low then insect lifespans may be low.

If the insect lifespan is low then it is less effective at disease transmission.

If humidity is low then the survival of filarial parasites may be reduced when they escape from the insect proboscis and transmission of this disease is reduced.

If the development project is in an area of low humidity and there will be a large scale increase in surface water then microclimate humidity will increase.

If the region is arid or semi-arid then schistosomiasis due to *S. mansoni* or *S. haematobium* is a potential health hazard.

Topography

If a river has a steep gradient then stream flow exposes bedrock (which provide breeding sites for various vectors).

If there is a flood plain and slowly meandering streams deposit silt then more permanent pools and marshes are created.

If there are fast currents and an unstable stream bed then the site is unfavourable for snails.

If bedrock is non-sedimentary then it is more suitable for blackfly breeding.

If land is levelled for road construction then borrow pits will be created.

If borrow pits fill with water then mosquito and snail habitats are created.

Rainfall

If there is plenty of rain then water contact may be reduced but snail breeding rates may be increased.

If an area has distinct dry and wet seasons then both insect vector density and disease prevalence are likely to have seasonal patterns.

If rainfall is plentiful in the river basin and hydrological conditions promote stream flow then stream margin breeding mosquito larvae will be flushed out but blackfly breeding sites may be enhanced.

If hydrological conditions cause rapid alterations in stream depth then rock pool breeding sites will be created as the stream falls and blackfly breeding sites may be created as the stream rises.

If there is plenty of rainfall and the soil is not too porous then temporary rainpools will be abundant.

If the vectors breed in temporary rainpools then their breeding sites will be very difficult to control.

If rainfall is less than expected then dried up river beds may serve as mosquito breeding sites.

Surface Water

If there is an abrupt margin between land and water then breeding sites are minimised.

If there is wave action and a steep shore or an unstable shore then mosquitoes and snails are deterred.

Geophysical

Soil type

If soil is compacted or ground cover is removed or soil is exposed to excessively dry conditions then soil loses its permeability or porosity and rainpools last longer.

If ground cover is removed then soil is eroded.

If soil is eroded then shallow pools are created by silt deposition.

If there are loess soils and semi-arid conditions then rodent reservoirs of leishmaniasis may be abundant.

If the soil is structurally poor then shallow latrine pits will collapse and provide vector breeding sites.

If the soil type is ferralsol or acrisol then there may be a lower incidence of malaria as compared with luvisols (because deep, free draining soils provide fewer pools for mosquitoes to breed).

Water Scarcity

If water is scarce or supply is irregular then there will be domestic water storage.

If tap water is too hot then it may be stored in domestic containers to cool.

If water is stored in domestic containers without good covers then container breeding mosquitoes such as *Aedes aegypti* will increase in abundance.

If there is a piped water supply and inadequate waste water disposal then there will be muddy surrounding water (in which mosquitoes and snails may breed).

If water pipes leak then mosquito breeding sites are created.

Irrigation Schemes

If an irrigation scheme is sited in a previously semi-arid region then health hazards are created because major ecological changes occur.

If molluscicide treatment is required then focal application can be very effective.

If old irrigation ditches are filled and new ones constructed alongside then snail populations are eradicated (oncomelanian snails were controlled in China by this method).

If canals are lined then the recurrent cost of vegetation and erosion control is reduced.

If water is piped then capital, maintenance and pumping costs are higher but health hazards are removed.

If sprinkler or drip feed irrigation is used then mosquitoes and snails are deterred.

If irrigation schemes are managed to provide the minimum of standing water for the minimum consecutive period then breeding can be controlled.

If canals and night stores are drained in a 7 day rotation with 2 days dry then mosquito breeding is reduced.

If a scheme is surrounded by afferent canals then the invasion of rodent populations is reduced.

Geophysical

Canalisation

If canal linings are imperfect then seepage pools will provide important breeding foci.

If rivers are crossed by fords, causeways or bridges then vector blackflies may be provided with new breeding sites.

If damage to canal banks is to be avoided then overpasses should be provided.

If the project is in West Africa then crossing points may attract tsetse flies.

If the mean flow rate is greater than 0.6 m/s and the channel is free of vegetation then snails are deterred (but erosion of unlined channels may occur).

If fast flow rates are to be maintained then regular desilting, bank repair and deweeding is necessary.

If the water is relatively clean and aerated and flowing then blackfly vectors may breed (Preferred habitats range from tiny streams and irrigation ditches to large rivers, to a depth of 0.15m. In W. Africa preferred flow rates are 0.7-1.2 m/s)).

If channels are designed for rapid draw-down and adequate drying-out then pooling during periods of low flow rate may be avoided.

If miracidia and cercaria are released in moving water then they cause infection downstream.

If solid waste collection facilities are inadequate then drains will be blocked by domestic waste.

If water is channeled through numerous small ditches then maintenance is more difficult than for a few large canals.

If an irrigation system contains night storage dams or canals then snail breeding should be expected (these habitats are difficult to treat with molluscicide).

If night storage dams become infested with aquatic vegetation then *Mansonia* mosquitoes should be expected.

Water Collections

If there are numerous small collections of clean water (such as are found in discarded cans, tyres, containers, leaf axils, tree holes, bamboo and rock pools) then *Aedes* mosquitoes may be abundant.

If borrow pits result from construction activities and fill with water then snails and mosquitoes may breed in them.

If borrow pits are deliberately planned as water holes then they should be enclosed and/or treated with larvicides or molluscicides.

Geophysical

Water Chemistry

If surface water is subject to high evaporation rates then salinity increases.

If a coastal site is occasionally inundated with seawater then saline pools are abundant.

If salinity is high then some species of mosquitoes are attracted and other mosquito species are repelled.

If nitrogen content is high then culicine mosquitoes may be more abundant than anophelines (exceptions include *An. varuna* and *An. annularis* in India).

If insecticide spraying kills non-target organisms then algal blooms may stimulate vector production.

If there is a lake outflow and algal blooms provide high nutrient levels then vector blackfly larvae may be abundant at the outflow.

If the calcium content is about 80ppm and there is a balance of calcium, potassium and magnesium and pH is slightly acid then aquatic snails may be abundant.

If stream nutrient content and chemistry is suitable then vector blackflies may be abundant.

If the water is turbid then important malaria vectors may be attracted but snails may be deterred (eg: by puddling soils in ricefields).

Drainage and Sullage

If domestic water is supplied without adequate provision for waste water disposal then a major public health hazard is created.

If an irrigation system has better maintained water supply ditches than drainage ditches then excess standing water may create a public health hazard.

If water is moderately polluted then snail populations are favoured.

If water is heavily polluted with human or animal faeces then culicine mosquitoes will be abundant.

If an approved latrine design is used then mosquito breeding may be minimised (recommended designs include ventilated improved pit latrines, vault latrines and pour-flush latrines).

Ground Water

If the water table is close to the surface then latrine pits will fill with water and promote culicine mosquito breeding.

If trees with high evapotranspiration potential are planted then the level of the water table may be reduced.

If the water table is very deep then vertical drainage may be used.

Geophysical

Impoundments

If a reservoir floods a stream course then blackfly breeding sites may be destroyed but new breeding sites may be created at the spillway.

If the spillway is constructed of undressed stone then blackfly breeding is likely.

If the spillway is vertical or overhung or siphoned then blackflies are deterred.

If the spillway flow is interrupted for at least 1 day in 7 by using twin spillways then blackfly breeding is unlikely.

If continuous discharge from a reservoir scours the stream bed then new blackfly breeding sites may be created downstream.

If blackflies disrupt dam construction then larvicide should be applied upto 20km up- and down-stream during periods of rising and falling flood.

If the water level of a reservoir can be varied then the breeding of mosquitoes and snails can be reduced (but fluctuating water levels favour some species of mosquito).

If a reservoir is deep then mosquitoes and snails will be deterred (they rarely occur in lakes and large ponds, except at shallow margins).

If land can be cleared before it is flooded then breeding sites may be much reduced (because there is more exposure to wave action).

If complete land clearance is too costly then clearance should be restricted to the vicinity of human habitation or water margins (clearance should extend above the projected shore-line).

If land is flooded then wild rodent populations are displaced and may be brought into closer contact with human communities.

If a dam is constructed for hydroelectricity generation then its water may not be available for irrigation when it is most required and water level variation is likely to be unpredictable.

If a dam is constructed without adequate vegetation clearance then rotting organic material will pollute downstream water and make it unsuitable for domestic use.

If habitations adjacent to water margins are sited facing prevailing on-shore winds then wave action renders the margin unsuitable for vector breeding.

If land is newly flooded then old mosquito breeding sites are flushed out but new breeding sites are eventually created (so mosquito abundance may initially fall before rising to new levels).

Biotic

Vegetation on site

If the banks of water courses are covered in vegetation then water flow rates are reduced and refuges provided for mosquitoes and snails.

If water is shaded or partly shaded by vegetation then certain mosquito species will be attracted (eg: *An. minimus* in Asia and *An. funestus* in Africa).

If water is not shaded then certain mosquito species will be attracted (eg: *An. gambiae* in Africa).

If there is tropical rain forest vegetation and shaded or partly shaded margins of forest pools and streams then *Anopheles* mosquitoes should be abundant.

If tropical rain forest is clear felled then shade breeding species are eliminated (but soil erosion and loss of resources occurs).

If tropical rain forest is selectively felled then disturbance of the ground creates additional breeding sites.

If crop production simplifies the vegetation environment then more dangerous vector and snail species may be encouraged.

If emergent or floating vegetation grows in deep water then vector breeding sites are created. (*Mansonia* mosquito larvae only breed in association with rooted or floating vegetation, especially *Eichhornia, Pistia* and *Salvinia*).

If the species of vegetation provide natural water containers then mosquitoes will breed in them (eg: Bromeliads including pineapples; bananas; bamboo; Colocacia and rotting tree stumps).

If there is halophytic[1] vegetation then there may be reservoir hosts of leishmaniasis (eg: the rodent *Psammomys obesus*).

Aquatic and terrestrial succession

If land or water is cleared of vegetation during the construction process then an orderly process of vegetational succession (regrowth) will occur.

If there is succession then vegetation will increase in size, density, cover and shade area (each phase in the succession will favour different species of animals, including vectors and their natural enemies).

If there are dense stands of vegetation then there are relatively humid resting places which are favoured by vectors.

---

1   Salt tolerant

Biotic

Farming systems

If oxen are replaced by tractors then mosquitoes which were feeding on oxen may be forced to bite people (a resurgence of malaria in Guyana was attributed to this factor).

If water buffaloes are replaced by tractors in a rice production system then removal of their bathing pools may affect dry season vector density.

If agricultural insecticides are used on a large scale then vectors may develop resistance to a wide range of insecticides (eg: *An. sinensis* in China, *An. sacharovi* in Turkey and *An. albimanus* in Central America).

Rice cultivation

If human settlements are close to rice fields then high rates of mosquito-borne disease may occur.

If a belt of dryland crops is established around a village then people are protected from rice-field breeding mosquitoes.

If paddy rice has been transplanted and is less than 75cm tall then malaria mosquitoes which prefer sunlit water will breed (eg: *An. arabiensis* in Africa, *An. freeborni* and *An. albimanus* in Central America).

If the paddy rice is taller than 75cm then shade loving malaria mosquitoes will breed (eg: *An. funestus* in Africa, *An. umbrosus* in S.E. Asia, *An. punctimaculata* in S. America).

If insecticides are used to kill rice pests and they kill aquatic predators then abundant mosquito breeding may result (eg: use of Dimecron at Ahero in Kenya).

If old plant debris is allowed to rot in newly flooded rice fields then mosquito breeding may be promoted (eg: *C. tritaeniorhynchus* in Sarawak).

If rice is planted in trenches through which water flows then mosquito breeding may be prevented (eg: *An. pseudopunctipennis* in Mexico).

Biotic

Rodent fauna

If an irrigation scheme is under development then rodent species which are closely associated with human settlements and are potential disease reservoirs will increase in abundance (eg: at Hola in Kenya abundance increased 10-50 times).

If an irrigation project raises the water table then rodents such as gerbils may become less abundant but associated sandflies may become more abundant (eg: a reservoir of cutaneous leishmaniasis which affected construction workers in Uzbekistan).

If previously unpopulated areas are settled then increased human contact with wild fauna may promote zoonoses.

If land is ploughed then colonial rodents such as *P. obesus* and *R. opimus* are eliminated but secondary reservoirs of leishmaniasis such as *Meriones* spp. may become more abundant.

If fodder crops are irrigated and it is a semi-arid region then rodents may increase in abundance.

Large fauna

If a settlement is planned and the settlers keep domestic animals then hygienic animal pens should be included in the settlement design.

If domestic animals are penned between human communities and mosquito breeding sites then mosquito vectors may bite the animals instead of the people and disease transmission is reduced.

Bird fauna

If wild ardeid birds such as herons are attracted to an irrigation project then there is a risk of arbovirus transmission such as Japanese encephalitis.

Aquatic fauna

If natural predators such as dragonfly nymphs and fish are numerous then they will contribute to the control of vectors.

If natural predators are contributing to vector control then they should be protected by careful choice of vector control measures such as insecticide and application schedule.

If certain fish are introduced into irrigation schemes then they can contribute to the control of vectors.

If fisheries are drained or rotated periodically then schistosomiasis hazards may be reduced.

Demographic and socio-cultural factors

Susceptibility to infection

If the demographic characteristics of the population are known then potential disease problems can be forecast with greater precision.

If a new settlement is developed then there will be more young fertile women and young children than in the rest of the population.

If there is a large population of children then schistosomiasis transmission is particularly favoured.

If future settlers are screened for parasitic disease then the chances of introducing new strains of parasites can be reduced.

If future settlers are screened on arrival, rather than at their place of origin, then anxiety, evasion and corruption may be reduced.

If the community has a high frequency of certain blood types such as haemoglobin S positive or Duffy group negative then malaria infections will be less severe.

If the population is largely immune to malaria then children and immigrants will be the main groups to suffer clinical illness.

If a labour force is assembled then the epidemic potential is increased.

If a susceptible community are translocated to a region with Japanese encephalitis and pig production is encouraged near to irrigation systems or reservoirs then there is a potential hazard of an epidemic (this has happened in Sri Lanka).

If use of antimalarial drugs is widespread then results of parasite surveys can be misleading.

If immigrants have no previous exposure to filariasis then clinical symptoms should be expected sooner than in communities from endemic areas (within 2 years in Indonesia).

If economic activities force certain people to expose themselves to the risk of infection then their health should be carefully monitored.

Social categories

If there are large groups of construction workers then up to ten times as many spontaneous immigrants may be attracted informally to provide goods and services.

If communities are displaced then they may be exposed to hazards to which they have no prior experience.

Customs

If rights to use a water source are traditionally vested in different interest groups then development of the water source may produce intergroup conflicts leading to the destruction of the project.

If anal cleansing customs involve wiping and a waste disposal system is designed which assumes washing then wiping materials may block the system.

Demographic and socio-cultural factors

Settlements

If there is inadequate provision for maintenance then piped water supplies and village pumps will be unreliable.

If the water supply is unreliable then water will be stored in the home (see water scarcity).

If water sources are far from the home then water will be stored in the home.

If water points are fitted with self-closing taps or handpumps then excess water discharge will be avoided.

If water supply and sanitation facilities are communal then there may be no incentive to maintain them properly.

If domestic waste water is not disposed of properly then vector and snail breeding sites are created.

If there are septic pools or surface grey water drainage or poorly maintained latrines then the mosquito vector of lymphatic filariasis may flourish.

If houses are designed to prevent mosquito ingress then much potential disease transmission can be avoided.

If house construction materials are absorbent then residual insecticide sprays will be less effective.

If settlements are sited 2km from swamps and forest margins then they are outside the flight range of most mosquitoes.

If settlements are sited far from agricultural zones then watchmen will be required to deter theft.

If there are locally breeding blackflies in a savannah or forest habitat then settlements should be sited at least 10km from the river.

If a dry-crop zone is sited around a settlement then contact with vectors which breed in irrigated sites is reduced.

If cultivation sites are far from permanent settlements then temporary settlements without proper sanitation will develop there.

Demographic and socio-cultural factors

Water contact

If small children bathe in irrigation systems where there are snails then schistosomiasis transmission will be intense.

If the climate is hot then the desire to bathe will outweigh any health education.

If snail-free bathing areas are provided and they are more convenient to use and their use is promoted by health education then schistosomiasis transmission can be reduced.

If bathing areas are sited in the centre of the village and they are closer to the home than irrigation canals then they are more likely to be used.

If bathing areas are to be kept free from snails then they should be refilled periodically and treated with molluscicide.

If the use of water sources near settlements is deterred by fencing, culverts, bridges and steep-sided canals then water contact is reduced.

If the daily cycle of water-related activities coincides with peak cercarial densities (the peaks are often during the middle of the day) then the risk of schistosomiasis infection is intensified.

If the seasonal cycle of activity (such as farming or fishing) coincides with peaks of vector or cercerial density then the risk of disease transmission is intensified.

Vector contact

If mosquito nets and screens are badly maintained then they are not effective.

If the climate is hot, humid and windless then mosquito nets and screens are unbearable.

If the farms are within 15km of a blackfly breeding site then farm workers will be bitten.

If a vector is largely confined to feeding on animals and it is not very abundant then it does not pose a major health hazard.

If a biting insect cannot support development of parasite then it may be a nuisance but it is not a health hazard.

If there are no local blackfly breeding then seasonal migration of potentially infected blackfly may cause a hazard within at least 1.5km of the river bank.

Infrastructure

Planning

If health care facilities are not upgraded in parallel with project development then they may not cope with the new demands which are imposed on them.

If there is a hierarchy of health facilities then it should include health workers and vector control workers at the village level.

If village level preventative measures are to be effective then the community must be actively involved in their design and operation.

If natural barriers are bridged or eliminated then vectors and diseases are able to spread into new areas.

If maintenance is to be effective then it must be envisaged at the design stage and adequately budgeted and appropriately organised and properly carried out.

If sanitation facilities are to be kept in good order then separate facilities will be required for each household.

If individual families or small communities are to improve their standards of hygiene then a credit facility may be required.

If economic activities depend on the production of vector breeding sites then control by legislation is impractical (eg: coir rope workers in India and Sri Lanka must soak coconut husks in pits which breed filariasis vectors).

If engineering plans are countersigned by a public health official then public health interests may be protected.

If funds for the operations of independent departments are inadequate then cooperation between departments suffers.

Organisation and Management

If there is no coordination of water supply and sanitation then excess standing water and septic pools will promote disease transmission.

If disease surveillance facilities are available then an early warning of vector-borne disease problems can be provided.

If equipment and supplies for vector control are to be stored then adequate theft proof facilities must be provided.

If health awareness is not promoted through education then preventative measures are not likely to succeed.

If unusual methods of water supply and sanitation are used then effective maintenance is essential.

If there is no system of solid waste disposal or no adequate system of food storage then rodents, houseflies and cockroaches will multiply.

If schistosomiasis transmission is to be interrupted then urine and faeces should be prevented from entering irrigation or drainage systems.

If refuse is tipped into water then breeding sites will be created.

If refuse is used for sanitary landfill then surface water can be reduced.

If there are health laws or ordinances which control mosquitogenic conditions and an effective infrastructure for ensuring compliance then the community can be protected from the actions of the individual.

If the control of breeding sites can be made into an economic activity then compliance is assured (eg: aquatic vegetation in India is being harvested for paper production).

Disease management by vector control

If endemic malaria is of high epidemic potential then residual insecticide may be effective.

If a vector rests outdoors then it cannot be controlled by house spraying unless there is also a repellent effect (have resting sites been checked recently?).

If there is a house spraying campaign and bedbugs are NOT controlled or beneficial predators are killed or the insecticide marks house furnishings or people develop allergies then expect non-compliance.

If a vector is controlled by insecticides then sooner or later it will develop physiological or behavioural resistance.

If insecticides are used to control agricultural pests then medical pests may develop resistance and natural control agents (such as fishes) may be killed.

If molluscicide is applied to irrigation canals then it will be inactivated before it reaches drainage channels (within 24-36 hours).

If biological control agents are used (parasites and predators) then periodic new releases will be required.

If fishes are used then fish holding tanks should be incorporated in the project design.

If larval control is undertaken then a skilled workforce is required.

If breeding sites are relatively few and easily accessible then source reduction is more likely to succeed.

If seasonal activity of vector is very brief then larval control is more likely to succeed.

Chapter 4

References, Glossary and Index

References

Readers are recommended to obtain the following additional publications. An address is listed.

Doumenge J.P., Mott K.E., Cheung C., Villenave D., Chapuis O., Perrin M.F. and G. Reaud-Thomas (1987). Atlas of the global distribution of schistosomiasis. Talence, CEGET-CNRS; Geneva, OMS/WHO; Talence, PUB, 400pp.

FAO (1984). Environmental Management for Vector Control in Rice Fields. Irrigation and Drainage Paper 41, pp152. Distribution and Sales Section, FAO, Via della Terme di Caracalla, 00100 Rome, Italy.

FAO (1987). Effects of agricultural development on vector-borne diseases. AGL/MISC/12/87. Address as above.

IRRI/PEEM (1988). Vector-borne Disease Control in Humans Through Rice Agroecosystem Management. Proceedings of the Workshop on Research and Training Needs in the field of Integrated Vector-borne Disease Control in Riceland Agroecosystems of Developing Countries, 9-14 March 1987. International Rice Research Institute in collaboration with PEEM. IRRI Communication and Publication Department, P.O. Box 933, Manila, Philippines.

PEEM (1987). Selected working papers for the third, fourth, fifth and sixth PEEM meeting. VBC/87.3, pp146. PEEM Secretariat, WHO, 1211 Geneva 27, Switzerland.

Tiffen, M. (1989). Guidelines for the incorporation of health safeguards into irrigation projects through intersectoral cooperation. VBC/89.5. PEEM Secretariat, WHO, 1211 Geneva 27, Switzerland.

WHO (1982). Manual on Environmental Management for Mosquito Control, with Special Emphasis on Malaria Vectors. WHO Offset Publication 66. pp283. WHO Distribution and Sales Service, 1211 Geneva 27, Switzerland.

WHO/EURO. (1983). Environmental Health Impact Assessment of Irrigated Agricultural Development Projects. World Health Organisation Regional Office for Europe, Scherfigsvej 8, Copenhagen 2100 DK 0, Denmark.

WHO (1989). Geographical distribution of arthropod-borne diseases and their principal vectors, document WHO/VBC/89.967, Geneva. Division of Vector Biology and Control, WHO, 1211 Geneva 27, Switzerland.

Additional Publications

Bottrell, D.G. (1979). Integrated Pest Management. Council on Environmental Quality, U.S. Government Printing Office, Washington D.C. 20402.

Cairncross, S. and Feachem, R.G. (1983). Environmental Health Engineering in the Tropics: An Introductory Text. Wiley. pp 283.

Colson, E. (1971). The Social Consequences of Resettlement. Manchester University Press.

Deom, J. (1982). Water Resources Development and Health: a selected bibliography. WHO, PDP/82.2 (mimeographed).

McJunkin, F.E. (1975). Water, Engineers, Development and Diseases in the Tropics. US AID, Washington.

PAHO (1982). Emergency Vector Control After Natural Disasters, PAHO Scientific Publications 419. PAHO, 525 Twenty-third Street, N.W., Washington D.C. 20037.

World Bank (1983). The Environment, Public Health and Human Ecology: Considerations for Economic Development. pp 294. The World Bank, 1818 H St. N.W., Washington DC 20433, USA.

WHO (1980). Epidemiology and Control of Schistosomiasis. Technical Report Series 643.

WHO (1980). Environmental Management for Vector Control. Technical Report Series 649.

WHO (1983). Integrated Vector Control. Technical Report Series 688, pp72, Geneva.

Glossary[1]

ABER	The Annual Blood Examination Rate is obtained by dividing total blood slides examined by total population size.
Anopheline	A mosquito of the subfamily which includes the genus *Anopheles*. May transmit malaria.
API	The Annual Parasite Index per 1000 population is obtained by dividing positive cases (x1000) by total population.
Arboreal	In trees.
Arbovirus	Arthropod-borne virus.
Arthropod	Includes insects, ticks and mites.
Assessment	A process of evaluating options which enables informed choices to be made between alternatives.
Bilharzia	Schistosomiasis, a parasitic disease acquired by contact with infected water.
Bromeliad	A plant in the family which includes pineapples. They often have small collections of water at the base of the leaves.
Cercariae	The infective stage of the *Schistosoma* parasite, free living in water.
Complex	A group of closely related species once thought to be a single species.
Culicine	A mosquito of the subfamily which includes the important genera *Aedes*, *Culex* and *Mansonia*. May transmit a number of diseases but never malaria.
Endemicity:	
endemic	Constant presence of a disease in a geographical area or community.

---

1   The definitions presented in this glossary are not official WHO definitions. They have been formulated with a view to explaining technical terms to a readership which is not routinely involved in health issues.

hypoendemic	Little transmission, effect on general population not important.
mesoendemic	The disease is found among small, rural communities with varying intensity depending on local circumstances.
hyperendemic	Intense, seasonal transmission where the immunity is insufficient to prevent the effect of disease on all age groups.
holoendemic	Perennial transmission of a high degree resulting in a significant immune response in all age groups, but particularly in adults.
Endophagy	Feeding indoors, opposite is exo-.
Endophily	Resting indoors, opposite is exo-.
Environmental manipulation	Making temporary changes to the environment with the objective of reducing vector abundance.
Environmental modification	Making permanent changes to the environment with the objective of reducing vector abundance.
Epiphyte	A plant growing on the branches of trees, such as bromeliads.
Filariasis	A parasitic infection caused by nematode worms.
Focus, plural foci	The origin(s) or source(s) of an infection or vector population.
Genus, plural genera	A category of biological classification comprising similar species; a rank between family and species.
Halophyte	A plant associated with saline environments.
Incidence	Number of new cases of disease over a defined period of time as a proportion of the population.
Intermediate host	The host occupied by juvenile stages of a parasite in which asexual reproduction frequently occurs.
Larvivorous fish	Fish species which feed preferentially on mosquito larvae. They may contribute significantly to the reduction of vector densities.

Malaria	A disease of humans caused by blood parasites of the species *Plasmodium falciparum, vivax, ovale* or *malariae* and transmitted by anopheline mosquitoes.
Marsh potential	A measure of a water bodies tendency to promote marshland.
Mitigate	To lessen the severity.
Molluscicide	A substance which kills molluscs such as snails.
Onchocerciasis	A disease caused by the parasitic filarial nematode *Onchocerca volvulus* also known as "river blindness".
Parasite	An organism dependent upon another living organism to which it is detrimental.
Pathogen	An organism or substance which causes disease.
Phlebotomine	A group of biting flies commonly called sandflies including the genus *Phlebotomus*, sometimes vectors of leishmaniasis.
Prevalence	The proportion of a population infected by a pathogen at a given moment.
Refractory	Resistant to ordinary treatment or infection.
Reservoir host	An animal species which carries a pathogen without detriment to itself and serves as a source of infection.
Resistance	An inherited ability of a pathogen or vector to survive treatment with a chemical designed to kill it. The following gradations are used in malaria terminology:
R1 resistance	Normal clinical response to drug treatment with recurrence of symptoms within 3 weeks because low level parasitaemia has gone undetected.
R2 resistance	Patient improves with treatment but parasites persist at detectable levels and clinical condition deteriorates if treatment ceases.
R3 resistance	No improvement in clinical condition or parasitaemia with treatment.
Safeguard	An activity intended to protect by preventing something from happening.

Simuliid	A family of biting flies commonly called blackflies including the important genus *Simulium*, sometimes vectors of onchocerciasis.
Schistosomiasis	A disease caused by parasites of the genus *Schistosoma*, also known as bilharzia, which has an aquatic snail intermediate host.
Spp.	species (plural).
SPR	Slide Positivity Rate is obtained by dividing positive blood slides by total slides examined.
Succession	The process of ecological change in which a habitat is colonised by a sequence of animal and plant species.
Susceptible	Prone to infection by parasites and pathogens.
Tabanid	A family of biting flies commonly called horseflies or deerflies, sometimes vectors of loiasis.
Tsetse	A biting fly found in Africa, genus *Glossina*, which may transmit sleeping sickness.
Trypanosomiasis	A disease caused by parasites of the genus *Trypanosoma* and including sleeping sickness in Africa and Chagas disease in Central and South America.
Vector	An organism which carries or transmits a pathogen.
Zoonosis	An infection of vertebrate animals transmissible to people.

Index

Y

Z

Appendix A

Worksheet 2

A checklist of the questions in the flowchart.

Project title _____

Project type _____

Location _____

Date of assessment _____

Project phase _____

Community group _____

Community Vulnerability

Which diseases are important?
_____
_____

How prevalent are they?
_____
_____

Is there drug resistance?
_____
_____

Is there a human or animal parasite reservoir?
_____
_____

Classifying the human community

How could the number of vulnerable people change as a result of the project?

_____
_____
_____
_____

Which communities are affected by the project?

_____
_____
_____

Which communities are susceptible to the specific diseases?

_____
_____
_____
_____

How will health status of each community be changed by the project?

_____
_____
_____
_____

Human behaviour

Does human behaviour favour contact with vectors or unsafe water?

_____
_____

Do people enter rural habitats for project or other work?

_____
_____

Do human activities at the project site present special problems?

_____
_____

Will the project change human behaviour?

_____
_____

Environmental Receptivity

How is the pathogen
usually transmitted?
_____

Which vector species are
important in the region?
_____
_____

Is the vector abundant?
_____
_____
_____

Does abundance vary
seasonally?
_____
_____

Are the vectors more
numerous in some places?
_____
_____

Are the vectors resistant
to any insecticides?
_____
_____

Could new species of
vectors colonise the site
from elsewhere?
_____
_____

Changes in vector abundance

Will the project affect
vector abundance?
_____
_____

Are the vectors abundant
on similar projects in the
region?
_____
_____
_____

How will the project affect
the number of vector
breeding sites?
_____
_____
_____

Could new species of
vectors colonise the site
from elsewhere
_____
_____

Contact associated with vector behaviour

Does vector behaviour favour contact with human communities?

_____
_____
_____

Do vector species associate with human communities?

_____
_____
_____

Do vectors inhabit undisturbed rural habitats?

_____
_____

Will the project affect vector behaviour?

_____
_____

Will settlement design affect vector abundance and contact?

_____
_____

Animal reservoirs

Is there an animal reservoir which could be affected by the project?

_____
_____

Will animals invade the project site?

_____
_____

Could the animal reservoir increase?

_____

Could the reservoir be eradicated?

_____
_____

Vigilance of the Health Services

Are there effective curative measures for the disease?

_____
_____
_____

Are curative measures locally available and effectively used?

_____
_____
_____

Are there effective prophylactic drugs and are they accessible?

_____
_____
_____

Can district health services cope with additional workloads created by the project?

_____
_____
_____

Vector control

Is there effective, routine control of medically important vectors in the project areas?

_____
_____

Are animal disease reservoirs controlled?

_____
_____

Is pesticide applied effectively?

_____
_____

Are vector populations monitored effectively?

_____
_____

Environmental management

Have vector control measures been incorporated in the project design or operating schedule?

_____
_____
_____
_____

Do any features of the design help to prevent vector breeding or contact?

_____
_____
_____
_____

Does the operating schedule ensure periodic destruction of breeding sites?

_____
_____
_____

Can contact with unsafe water be avoided?

_____
_____
_____
_____

Can the project design be modified so as to reduce health hazards?

_____
_____
_____
_____

Appendix B

Questions grouped by specialist

Checklist of questions to be asked at the Ministry of Health, other government departments and elsewhere.

Project planners

What is the size of each human group associated with the project? Can design be changed to prevent introduction of vector breeding sites or animal disease reservoirs? Are medical care facilities incorporated in project design?

Will people venture into rural habitats in which there is a risk of disease transmission? Will project change human activities and settlement density?

Have settlements been properly sited?

Are there any similar projects in the region? Which officers are responsible for the management of these other projects?

Managers of similar projects in the region

What reservoir animals, vector and host species are associated with the project? How are the medical pests controlled? What disease problems are associated with the project? What preventative, curative or mitigation measures are required? What features of the design or operating schedule help to prevent vector breeding? What human groups are affected by the project?

Ministry of Health and specialist units

Which vector-borne diseases occur in this region? Is there a local entomologist or pest control officer who can be contacted? Is there a local game or animal control officer who can be contacted? How prevalent is the vector-borne disease in question? Is the project likely to lead to increase of the disease and why? Are there any foci of drug resistance? Is the disease locally resistant to drug therapy?

For each human group affected by the project, are they likely to be susceptible or immune to the disease? Is the health status of each group likely to lead to a change in susceptibility?

Is there an animal disease reservoir?

Are there effective preventative measures? Can the disease be effectively diagnosed and treated under local conditions? Can district services cope with the additional workloads created by the project? Are there sufficient supplies of drugs and equipment? Are prophylactic drugs available?

Are treatment facilities accessible to local people? Are prophylactic drugs used effectively by most of the people? Are susceptible human groups protected from infection? Are there charts and maps showing the prevalence of disease in different locations and seasons?

Are there any plans to screen migrants?

Entomologist, vector control department or pest control officer

Which vector or host species is usually involved with the disease in question? Are these vectors or hosts known to be present at or near project site, at least seasonally or in discrete foci?

What are the preferred breeding sites of locally important vector and host species? Which species is associated with each category of site? Are breeding sites abundant permanently or seasonally? Which season? Will the project create additional classes of breeding sites?

Are the vectors abundant upwind or upstream of the site? How far away? Is long distance migration of the vector expected? Is passive migration by vehicles or livestock expected?

Do the vectors or hosts inhabit undisturbed rural environments? Is there a control programme against the vector population in the project area? Will the project change vector behaviour?

Can contact between people and the vector be reduced or avoided? Is the vector control programme effective?

Is there effective local pesticide application?

Local community affected by the project

Have you been informed about the project and its implications for your dwelling place and livelihood? What modifications would you like to make to the project plans and why?

Do you visit uninhabited areas very often? Do you sleep there at night? Where are your gardens? Do you engage in hunting and gathering activities? What wild animals are present in the project area?

What diseases do you fear and how do you believe that they are contracted? Do you know a community health volunteer?

What health facilities are available to you? How often do you use them? How much does it cost you to get there? How much do you spend on medicine? Do you use repellents or malaria prophylaxis? Do you use bednets?

Does the government try to spray your house? How often? What for? Do you allow your house to be sprayed? Does it work? Are there any unpleasant effects of spraying?

Do you employ other people to work for you? If so, where do they live?

If it is practical to obtain rather more personal information without causing offence it might be appropriate to determine people's washing habits, social activities and sleeping customs.

Game or animal control officer or department

Is there an animal disease reservoir at or near the project site? What species? Have the animal reservoir species been attracted to similar projects? Can the animal reservoir be controlled or eradicated? Will project increase the size of the reservoir population?

Appendix C

Fact Sheets

For easy reference, fact sheets have been included on ten vector-borne diseases of relevance to water resource development. The diseases are listed in the following order:

- Schistosomiasis
- Malaria
- Yellow Fever
- Lymphatic Filariasis
- Onchocerciasis
- Dengue and Dengue Haemorrhagic Fever
- Visceral Leishmaniasis
- Cutaneous Leishmaniasis
- Japanese Encephalitis
- African Trypanosomiasis

Fact sheet for Schistosomiasis

Common name	Bilharzia
Type of causal organism	Blood fluke, genus *Schistosoma*.
Important species	*Schistosoma haematobium, mansoni* and *japonicum*.
Vector	Aquatic snails mainly of the genera *Bulinus, Biomphalaria* and *Oncomelania*, respectively .
Transmission	Human contact with water containing infective stages which are shed from infected snails. Contact often occurs while bathing.
Environment	Fresh water associated with irrigation schemes, reservoirs and water holes.
Effect on human health	Heavily infected individuals feel unwell and weak and may have seriously diseased liver or bladder.
Diagnosis	Eggs are found in stool (*mansoni* and *japonicum*) and urine (*haematobium*).
Treatment	Effective curative drugs are available.
Economic importance	An estimated 200 million people are infected but heavy infection is patchy. However, both the distribution and the number of heavy infections are increasing.
Vector control	Removal of snail habitats or killing snails with chemicals.
Prevention	Provision of safe water sources and proper sanitation, reduced contamination of water with human faeces and urine, changes in human behaviour.

Fact sheet for Malaria

Type of causal organism	Blood protozoon, genus *Plasmodium*
Important species	*Plasmodium falciparum, vivax, ovale* and *malariae.*
Vector	Mosquitoes of the genus *Anopheles*. There are one or two important species in each region.
Transmission	By the bite of mosquitoes which previously fed on infected humans.
Environment	Within 1-2kms of suitable breeding sites which include a wide variety of relatively clean water, depending on species. The mosquito bites at night.
Effect on human health	Fever and weakness are common. *P. falciparum* infection can lead to death if untreated. Partial immunity after long exposure.
Diagnosis	Examination of blood films.
Treatment	Effective prophylactic and curative drugs are available but there is increasing drug resistance.
Economic importance	Many hundreds of millions of people are infected or exposed but partial immunity is widespread. Can seriously undermine development projects, especially when non-immune settlers are involved.
Vector control	Source reduction; residual house spraying; environmental management.
Prevention	Prophylaxis; personal protection using bednets and repellents; vector control.

Fact sheet for Yellow Fever

Type of causal organism	Virus
Vector	Mosquito of the genus *Aedes*. A common species is *Aedes aegypti*.
Transmission	By the bite of mosquitoes which previously fed on infected humans or monkeys.
Environment	Either forests inhabited by monkeys or urban areas where the mosquito breeding site is artificial containers. The mosquito bites by day.
Effect on human health	Many infections may not produce symptoms but others are very serious.
Diagnosis	Difficult and specialised.
Treatment	Supportive only.
Economic importance	Occasional epidemics with widespread sickness and death.
Vector control	In urban areas artificial containers should be destroyed or emptied twice per week. Insecticidal fogging can be used to halt an epidemic.
Prevention	By vector control and vaccination of the human population.

Fact sheet for Lymphatic Filariasis

Common name	Elephantiasis, Bancroftian filariasis, Brugian filariasis.
Type of causal organism	Filarial worms
Important species	*Wuchereria bancrofti, Brugia malayi.*
Vector	Mosquitoes of the genera *Anopheles, Aedes, Culex* and *Mansonia.* In urban areas the vector is usually *Culex quinquefasciatus* which breeds in water polluted with sewage.
Transmission	By the bite of mosquitoes which previously fed on infected humans or, in one very restricted area, on wild animals.
Environment	Mainly urban. Mainly night biting.
Effect on human health	Repeating fever. Legs and sometimes genitals become very swollen and infected in later stages.
Diagnosis	Detection of the worm larvae in a blood film.
Treatment	Oral administration of a cheap and effective drug known commonly as DEC.
Economic importance	Many millions of people are infected but are not sick while others suffer repeated fever. People with swollen limbs suffer much distress and have difficulty moving about.
Vector control	Source reduction by drainage and larviciding in urban areas; residual house spraying.
Prevention	By vector control or contact prevention.

Fact sheet for Onchocerciasis

Common name	River blindness
Type of causal organism	Filarial worm
Important species	*Onchocerca volvulus*
Vector	Blackflies of the genus *Simulium*. Important species include members of the *Simulium damnosum complex*.
Transmission	By the bite of blackflies which previously fed on infected humans. They bite during the day.
Environment	Within about 10kms of rivers and streams where the flies breed in clean, well aerated, fast flowing water.
Effect on human health	Intense itching, skin changes and swelling with blindness in the later stages.
Diagnosis	Examination of skin snips.
Treatment	Oral administration of a newly developed drug called Ivermectin.
Economic importance	Fear of blindness causes people to leave the river valleys. Severe disability due to blindness.
Vector control	Aerial spraying of breeding sites. Design of spillways and canals to reduce breeding.
Prevention	Repellents; vector control.

Fact sheet for Dengue and Dengue Haemorrhagic Fever

Common name	Dengue and Dengue Haemorrhagic Fever (DHF)
Type of causal organism	Virus
Vector	Mosquitoes of the genus *Aedes*. A common species is *Aedes aegypti*.
Transmission	Human contact with day biting mosquitoes.
Environment	Urban areas, houses and gardens.
Effect on human health	Often affects children. DF is relatively mild but DHF is a serious complication requiring hospitalization and frequently results in death.
Diagnosis	Difficult and specialised.
Treatment	Supportive only.
Economic importance	Increasing numbers of epidemics in many tropical and sub-tropical areas. Great public concern.
Vector control	Destruction or emptying artificial containers twice per week. Insecticidal fogging can be used to halt an epidemic.
Prevention	Vector control.

Fact sheet for Visceral Leishmaniasis

Common name	Kala Azar
Type of causal organism	Protozoon of the genus *Leishmania*.
Important species	*Leishmania donovani*
Vector	Sandflies, genus *Phlebotomus* in the Old World and genus *Lutzomyia* in the new world.
Transmission	Bite of sandfly. Animal reservoir in rodents and canines as well as people.
Environment	In and around houses in India, more rural areas elsewhere.
Effect on human health	Enlargement of liver and spleen. Can cause death if untreated.
Diagnosis	Detection of parasites in organ samples. Detection of antibodies.
Treatment	Supervised administration of drugs with toxic side-effects.
Economic importance	Epidemics have occurred in India but elsewhere cases are sporadic.
Vector control	Residual house spraying with insecticides where transmission is domestic.
Prevention	Destruction of canine reservoirs; vector control; repellents; resiting villages.

Fact sheet for Cutaneous Leishmaniasis

Common names	Oriental sore, Espundia, Chiclero's ulcer
Type of causal organism	Protozoon of the genus *Leishmania*.
Important species	*Leishmania tropica, major, braziliensis*
Vector	Sandflies, genus *Phlebotomus* in the Old World and genus *Lutzomyia* in the new world
Transmission	Bite of sandfly. Many reservoir animals, especially colonial rodents.
Environment	Semi-arid regions where irrigation is likely; S. American forests.
Effect on human health	Open sore, self-healing in some regions, more serious in others.
Diagnosis	Microscopic examination of stained material extracted from the ulcer.
Treatment	Self-healing forms require no special treatment. Supervised administration of drugs with toxic side-effects.
Economic importance	Serious outbreaks reported on water development projects in some semi-arid regions.
Vector control	Residual house spraying.
Prevention	Destruction of animal reservoirs; vaccination.

Fact sheet for Japanese Encephalitis

Common name	J.E.
Type of causal organism	Virus
Vector	Mosquitoes in the genus *Culex*.
Transmission	Bite of mosquito. Animal reservoir in pigs and birds such as herons and egrets.
Environment	Ricefields. Night biting mosquitoes.
Effect on human health	Serious mental disturbances leading to brain damage and death. In epidemics children are the main victims.
Diagnosis	Difficult and specialised.
Treatment	Supportive only.
Economic importance	Only a small percentage of infected people develop symptoms. Epidemics could severely disrupt irrigation projects.
Vector control	Ricefield breeding mosquitoes are difficult to control.
Prevention	Avoid pig rearing near irrigation schemes; environmental management.

Fact sheet for African Trypanosomiasis

Common name	Gambian and Rhodesian Sleeping Sickness
Type of causal organism	Protozoon of the genus *Trypanosoma*.
Important species	*Trypanosoma gambiense* and *rhodesiense*
Vector	Tsetse flies, genus *Glossina*.
Transmission	There is an animal reservoir in some regions.
Environment	Savannah woodland and riverain vegetation of Sub-saharan Africa. The fly bites during the day.
Effect on human health	Mental disturbances, brain damage and death.
Diagnosis	Detection of parasite in blood film or other parts of the body.
Treatment	Supervised administration of drugs with toxic side-effects.
Economic importance	A similar disease is a major constraint on cattle production. The human disease is usually sporadic but devastating epidemics continue to occur.
Vector control	Environmental management; insecticide spraying; trapping.
Prevention	Prophylaxis; active case finding where no animal reservoir; reduced fly contact.

Computerised versions of this text are available

Please write for more information to the address below enclosing the following details.

What size disks do you use?	5¼" ☐	3½" ☐
Do you have a hard disk?	Yes ☐	No ☐
Is your computer IBM compatible?	Yes ☐	No ☐
Do you use a mouse?	Yes ☐	No ☐
Do you have a graphics screen?	Yes ☐	No ☐

The following packages are being developed and we would appreciate your comments. Which would be of most benefit to you or your organisation?

Computer assisted instruction. ☐
Computer assisted decision support. ☐
Computer assisted quick reference. ☐

Which implementation would you consider most useful?

A hypertext system ☐
An expert system ☐
Don't know ☐

**Dr M. H. Birley, WHO Collaborating Centre: Environmental Management for Vector Control,
Department of Medical Entomology,
Liverpool School of Tropical Medicine, Pembroke Place,
Liverpool L3 5QA, United Kingdom.**

A flowchart concerning Community Vuln

Current health status of the
community

Which diseases are important
in the region?

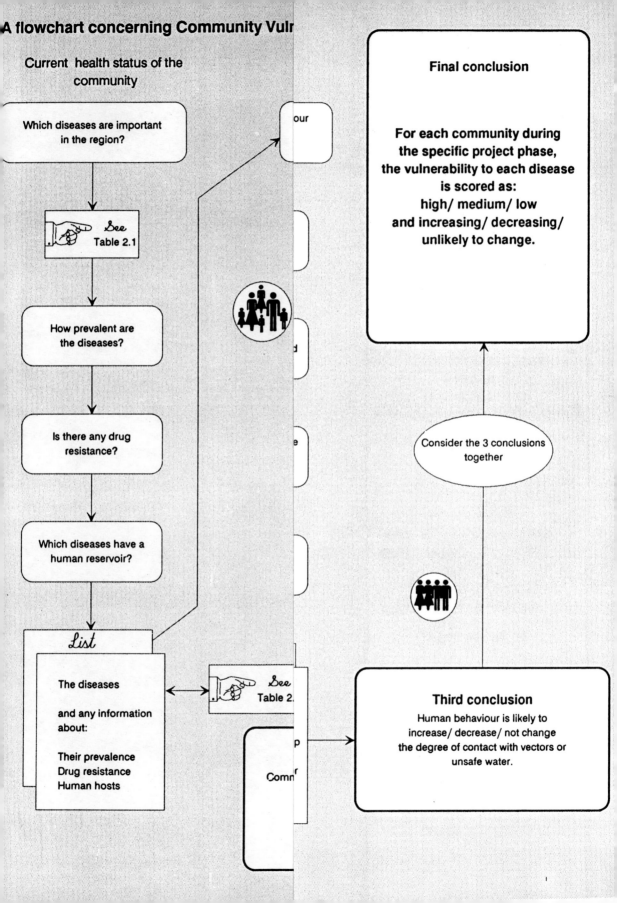

See
Table 2.1

How prevalent are
the diseases?

Is there any drug
resistance?

Which diseases have a
human reservoir?

List

The diseases

and any information
about:

Their prevalence
Drug resistance
Human hosts

See
Table 2.

Comm

our

Final conclusion

**For each community during
the specific project phase,
the vulnerability to each disease
is scored as:
high/ medium/ low
and increasing/ decreasing/
unlikely to change.**

Consider the 3 conclusions
together

Third conclusion
Human behaviour is likely to
increase/ decrease/ not change
the degree of contact with vectors or
unsafe water.

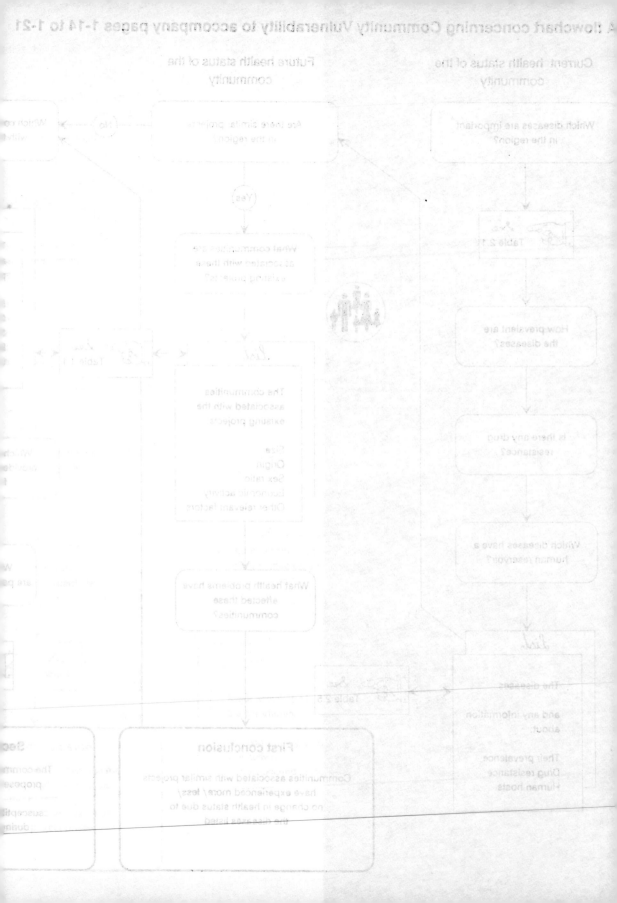

Current st...
enviro...

hat vector spec...
ith the existing ...
nder community...

Are the vecto...
or perennially...

Are the vecto...
generally dis...

Are the vec...
near house...
undisturbe...

Is there any...
resista...

List...

Disease
Vector type...
Vector spe...
Seasonality...
Focality
Domesticit...
Pesticide r...